Belknap's Waterproof AL NEW EXPANDED EDITION

Grand Canyon R

Buzz Belknap / Loie Belknap

MW00629168

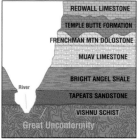

GEOLOGY 4

How was the Grand Canyon formed? How many millions of years did it take? What processes are still going on? Easy-to-understand text, full-color diagrams and photos graphically describe the natural forces at work.

WHITEWATER WORKSHOP 26

Getting your feet wet is just the beginning. Learn to distinguish an *eddy* from a *hole,* a *tongue* from a *sleeper.* Find out some basic river facts before you climb into the boat. How to find latest commercial and private boating information.

HISTORY 30

Major Powell and his men first explored the Canyon in 1869. Since then many courageous men and women have followed in his wake. Meet some of those who have added their tales to the story of the Grand Canyon.

RIVER MAPS 34

A wealth of river lore and legend accompanies these highly detailed and informative shaded relief and contour maps. Rapids are readily identifiable, with river miles and features carefully keyed.

ARCHAEOLOGY & NATIVE PEOPLES 86

The *Puebloans* came and left. The *Paiute* once hunted its valleys and rims. The *Cohonina* tried to farm it, and mysteriously disappeared. Discover these first Canyon visitors, and those, like the *Hualapai* and *Havasupai,* who remain.

NATURAL HISTORY 96

From *chuckwalla* to *bighorn sheep*, from *ocotillo* to *Mormon tea*—the sometimes harsh and unyielding Canyon environment has created a diversity of survivors. Full-color photos of flora and fauna will help you identify the denizens.

BILL BELKNAP'S PHOTO WORKSHOP 120

If you want to take great photos of your river trip, read this no-nonsense, non-technical, practical guide to shooting the best— no matter what your equipment. Takes you from the idea to the edit, the shutter click to the slideshow—painlessly.

For Bill & Fran Belknap

Photo Above:
Toroweap Overlook,
River Mile 177
NATIONAL PARK SERVICE

Published by:

 **WESTWATER BOOKS**

A division of Belknap Photographic Services, Inc.
Evergreen, Colorado 80439.

Credits
Design and cartography: Buzz Belknap
Text: Bill Belknap, Loie Belknap Evans, Lynn Evans Peesel, Wayne Ranney,
     Meribeth Riffey, Douglas W. Schwartz
Co-Editor: Jodi Parry Belknap; Managing Editor: Loie Belknap Evans
Production Assistant: Richard Hepburn
Geology Consultant: George Billingsley

(Crew Page)
See page 127 for more detailed descriptions of contributors.

Manuscript and Map Review: Diane Boyer; O'Connor Dale; Day DeLaHunt; Brad Dimock; John Evans; R.J. Johnson; ML and Richard Quartaroli; Philip M. Smith; and National Park Service personnel.

Special Appreciation to: Cline Library Special Collections NAU; Grand Canyon National Park; U.S. Geological Survey (GCMRC); and to the late Otis "Dock" Marston for sharing his river research and photographs.

Heartfelt Thanks to: family and all the friends—old and new; talented photographers, outfitters, river guides, and government agency personnel, whose collective contributions helped build this book. We could not have done it without their support.

Additional Acknowledgements
Contents page—dory photo, Allen Gilberg; claret-cup cactus, Glenn Rink. Geologic computer illustrations pages 14-17 by Kym L. Miller; computer colorization of some historical photos by Buzz Belknap; pen and ink drawings of Bright Angel Pueblo and Rampart Cave sloth by Scott Matsushige.

Library of Congress Control Number: 2017901116
ISBN-13: 978-0-916370-24-4

Printed in China

"Widforss Want-a-be"
SERENA SUPPLEE

GEOLOGY OF THE GRAND CANYON

by WAYNE RANNEY

CHARLY HEAVENRICH

Lees Ferry
Gateway to a Grand
Canyon geologic
adventure.

NPS PHOTO BY MARK LELLOUCH

No one escapes the Grand Canyon without being touched by some aspect of its splendid geologic story. The marvelous display of rocks and the earth history they reveal make the Canyon a perfect geologic classroom.

To better understand the geology of the Canyon, this narrative focuses on four parts: the deposition of the rock layers; the evolution of the Colorado River; the fascinating manner in which the Grand Canyon was carved; and finally the dramatic lava flows in the lower end of the Canyon. Each part of the story captivates the relatively few people who annually see the Canyon by river (27,000 out of 6 million total park visitors).

It involves a long span of time when the Grand Canyon region was near sea level; a much shorter interval when the rocks were uplifted; and a surprisingly brief time when the river cut the Canyon and was partially filled with lava. The story is as thrilling as the ride you are about to undertake!

The Rocks

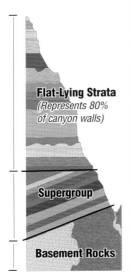

Flat-Lying Strata
(Represents 80% of canyon walls)

Supergroup

Basement Rocks

Rock Sequence Diagram
See pages 16-17 for detailed diagram

Formations are named after a specific place where they were first studied and described. Tapeats Sandstone, for example, was first described in a tributary called Tapeats Canyon.

While the story of the modern Colorado River involves only tens of millions of years, the history of the rocks within Grand Canyon goes back hundreds of millions or even billions of years. During much of this time, the Grand Canyon region was located near sea level which explains why so much rock strata is preserved here. Sediments are constantly being eroded and washed down from mountainous areas, but they only become preserved as stratified rock layers if they come to rest in a part of the earth's crust that is actively subsiding, usually along the shorelines of the continents. This subsidence creates the vertical space for more and more sediment to accumulate, where it becomes buried and hardened into sedimentary rocks. Even though strata are buried for most of their existence, they retain a record of the surface setting in which they were deposited.

The diagram on pages 16-17 illustrates the great stack of rocks present in the Grand Canyon. Note that three different rock sequences are shown: flat-lying strata that make up the bulk of the canyon walls; an inclined set of strata below these; and, farther below, a completely different package of rock that is metamorphic and igneous in origin. Each rock unit (a *formation* to a geologist) records the multiple environments that once existed here, while the gaps that exist between the three packages (called *unconformities*) record distinct periods of mountain building and erosion.

The oldest rocks in the Grand Canyon are between 1.84 and 1.65 billion years old and are considered part of the basement of the North American continent. They originated as layers of sandstone, shale, or volcanic rock that ultimately became buried, deformed, and altered in a great collision between ancient North America and other pieces of the earth's crust. During collision, the rocks were folded deep into the crust where they were altered by heat and pressure (*metamorphosed*) forming the Vishnu Schist. Deeper still, other rocks melted completely forming magma, which rose upward and intruded into the schist, creating a pink-colored igneous rock called Zoroaster Granite. Geologists believe that the metamorphism occurred some 13 miles below the surface and that ancient mountains most likely capped the Grand Canyon region at this time. These basement rocks are seen today in the deep recesses of the Upper, Middle, and Lower Granite gorges, and are first encountered below Hance Rapid at river mile 78.

How cliffs and slopes are formed

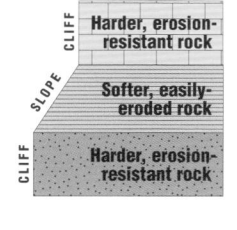

CLIFF | Harder, erosion-resistant rock
SLOPE | Softer, easily-eroded rock
CLIFF | Harder, erosion-resistant rock

How rocks are formed

Igneous rocks
are cooled from a molten state. *For example,* granite, basalt, pegmatite.

Sedimentary rocks
are deposited as particles by water, or sometimes by wind or streams. *For example,* limestone, sandstone, shale.

Metamorphic rocks
are changed over time from a pre-existing rock type by heat, pressure, and chemical activity. *For example,* marble from limestone, quartzite from sandstone, slate from shale.

During the next 400 plus million years, erosion attacked and destroyed these ancient mountains. The confining weight that was removed by erosion allowed the rocks below to progressively rise. In this way, the Vishnu Schist was eventually brought up to the Earth's surface. Erosion smoothed the topography and it was on this subdued surface that a sequence of strata two-and-a-half miles thick was deposited. These layers, called the Grand Canyon Supergroup, were laid down between about 1,254 and 740 million years ago, and contain evidence for shallow marine, coastal dune, sluggish river, and volcanic environments. These layers were later subjected to faulting that disrupted and tilted the strata. Some blocks were faulted down and buried, thus escaping the 200 plus million years of erosion that followed. This is why the Supergroup rocks are found today in only a few localities in Grand Canyon. These exquisitely colored and tilted rocks are a playful diversion in a canyon known for its flat-lying strata; the best exposures are seen at river level between river miles 63 to 78, and 131 to 139.

The upper 80 percent of the walls of Grand Canyon expose many horizontally stratified rocks that record numerous ancient landscapes that once existed here. These strata also are present outside the confines of Grand Canyon, allowing geologists to decipher the ancient geography of the widespread area surrounding it. The detailed paleographic maps on the page below show what this part of the southwestern landscape used to look like. These ancient environments include wave-washed beaches (Tapeats Sandstone), tropical seas teeming with sea life (Redwall Limestone), and vast Sahara-like deserts (Coconino Sandstone).

Vishnu Schist & Zoroaster Granite

Tapeats Sandstone

Birdseye view of Tonto Plateau looking upstream from mile 90 shows 505 million year old Tapeats Sandstone atop 1,750 million year old Vishnu Schist and Zoroaster Granite illustrating the Great Unconformity or missing chapter of over a billion years of geologic history.

NPS PHOTO

"ANCIENT LANDSCAPES OF THE COLORADO PLATEAU"

Maps courtesy of Ron Blakey and Wayne Ranney

(State lines and modern Colorado and Green rivers are shown for reference only)

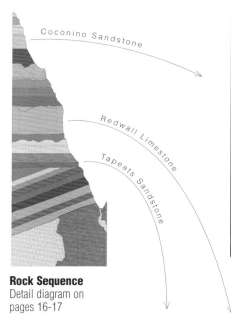

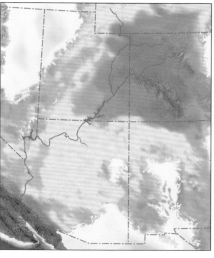

Coconino Sandstone 275 million years ago
Sahara-like desert environment of the
Coconino Sandstone.

Rock Sequence
Detail diagram on
pages 16-17

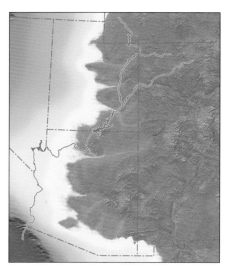

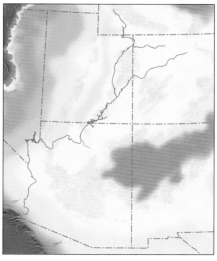

Tapeats Sandstone 505 million years ago
Beach environment in Arizona where the Tapeats
Sandstone was deposited.

Redwall Limestone 340 million years ago
Widespread, shallow marine environment
for the Redwall Limestone.

Colorado River

Total length: 1,450 mi

Grand Canyon length: 278 mi

RIVER ELEVATION AT:
Lees Ferry: 3,100 ft
Phantom Ranch: 2,400 ft
Grand Wash Cliffs: 925 ft*

Elevation change in
Grand Canyon: 2,175 ft*

*(*Before Hoover Dam*)

Average gradient in Grand
Canyon: 8 feet per mile

Average width: 300 feet

Minimum width: 76 feet

Maximum measured
depth: 110 feet

Average depth: 35 feet

Maximum flow - bgcd
(before Glen Canyon
Dam): 300,000 cfs (est)

Average annual
sediment load (bgcd):
168 million tons

C ompared to other North American rivers, the Colorado River is not particularly large in volume, yet its name evokes images of furious whitewater, stunning red rock scenery, and thirsty cities fighting for every drop of precious water. The Colorado begins near the Continental Divide at 14,000 feet. A drop of rainwater that falls here will either go down the river to the Pacific Ocean, or into the Mississippi River system to the Atlantic Ocean. From its initial alpine setting the Colorado winds some 1,450 miles across the upland desert known as the Colorado Plateau and eventually dries up near the cactus-studded deserts that border the Gulf of California. Remarkably, no water from the Colorado reaches the sea today—every drop is used by cities and farms or lost to reservoir evaporation.

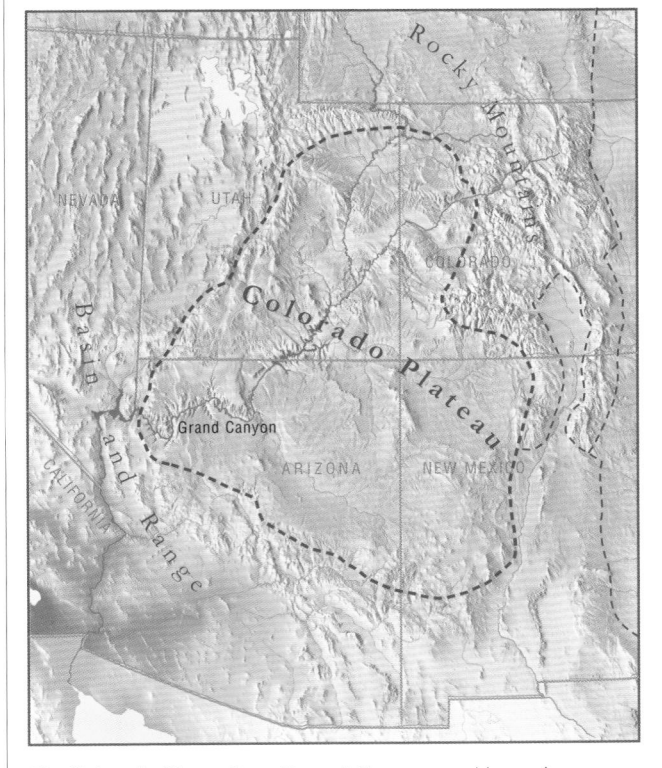

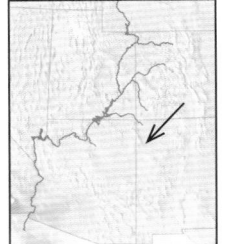

Today's Southwest Drainage

The Colorado River slices through three geographic provinces on its way to the sea: the Rocky Mountains, Colorado Plateau and the Basin and Range.

The geologic history of the river is key to the formation of the Grand Canyon, but the river and its ancestors may be far older than the Canyon itself. The last time the sea was present in the region was about 70 to 80 million years ago. When this sea retreated, a blank canvas was exposed upon which an initial river system was painted. Surprisingly, this early river system flowed to the northeast, opposite its direction today.

River gravels exposed in the western Grand Canyon provide good evidence for the flow direction of this ancestral river system. Most geologists agree with this interpretation, which covers a time from about 80 to 30 million years ago, noting that the gravel types could only have come from the south with the bedding textures indicating northeast flow.

Ancient Northeast Drainage

MAP COURTESY RON BLAKEY & WAYNE RANNEY

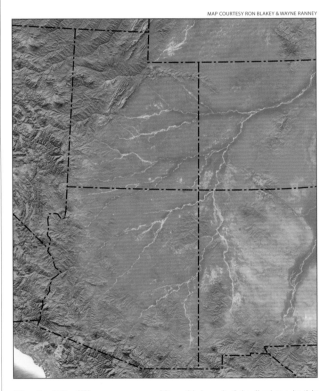

Map for 70 million years ago. After withdrawal of the final sea in this area about 70 million years ago, an initial northeast drainage system was established. The evolution and ultimate reversal of this system led to the development of the modern Colorado River.

THE COLORADO RIVER

Water Saw and Conveyor Belt

Acting as a sand and water saw, as well as a conveyor belt, the Colorado River carried away more than a million cubic yards of sediment annually before modern dams provided settling basins along the way. Man-made dams, while serving to impound water for various human purposes, also control the enormous floods which once flushed the Canyon periodically, and replaced beaches important to river runners and Grand Canyon ecology.

Much of the mystery surrounding the evolution of the Colorado River itself relates to the fact that there is no direct record of it from about 24 to nearly 6 million years ago. We know that the initial northeast system of drainage had to be altered or reversed during this 18 million year period but the exact mechanism, or combination of mechanisms, and the timing of such a drainage reversal is unresolved.

Only at about 6 million years ago does evidence of the modern Colorado River suddenly appear on the landscape in the form of distinctive deposits found downstream from Grand Canyon. These deposits show that the modern Colorado was headed southwest toward the Gulf of California. The Gulf itself was formed by movement on the San Andreas Fault, which split Baja California away from mainland North America. Today, farmers near the Salton Sea grow crops in eroded material from the Grand Canyon and Rocky Mountains.

Debris Flows

Nearly all of the Canyon's rapids are formed by a special type of flood called a debris flow (exceptions are Bedrock at mile 131—and several formed by rockfall—MNA at mile 27.1, Nixon Rock at mile 100.4, and Sinyella at mile 154). A thick slurry of roughly equal parts water and sediment, a debris flow can easily move car-size boulders. In December 1966, at Mile 99, a debris flow roared down Crystal Creek into mild Crystal Rapid, instantly transforming it into one of the most challenging runs on the river. In pre-dam years, large floods on the river would disperse the smaller boulders downstream, lessening the severity of the

rapid. As recurring side canyon debris flows bring more boulders into the channel, Crystal and other rapids may continue to grow in size and difficulty. In effect, man's damming of the river has increased the adventure of river running.

USGS - GCMRC PHOTO

Crystal Rapid was instantly transformed into one of the most challenging runs on the river by a debris flow in December 1966.

The Grand Canyon

Length: 278 mi

Width: 10 mi (avg.)
18 miles (max.)

Depth: 1 mile
5,280 feet (avg.)
6,000 feet (max.)

Volume of rock eroded:
803 cubic miles

North Rim Elevation:
8,200 feet

South Rim Elevation:
7,000 feet

North Rim Precipitation:
25 inches/yr

South Rim Precipitation:
20 inches/yr

Phantom Ranch
Precipitation: 8 inches/yr

Annual Visitation:
6,000,000 (approx)

Annual River Runners:
27,000 (approx)

B y about 70 million years ago, the Grand Canyon region began its rise above sea level. Since then as much as 10,000 feet of Mesozoic rock have been removed by erosion. However, part of these strata remains in the cliffs above Lees Ferry. Erosion carved through an additional one mile thickness of rock to create the Grand Canyon. (See Step 8 on page 15.) To date, geologists do not agree precisely on how or when this carving began, but an age of 6 million years is most often acknowledged. This date, however, refers specifically to the age of the modern Colorado River and does not necessarily speak to those portions of the Canyon that could have been formed earlier by an ancestor of the modern river.

Part of the difficulty in determining an age or mechanism for the Canyon's development is that the river works as a great excavator, removing much of the evidence of its early history. Another problem is that the natural processes that eroded the Canyon were often operating in environments different from those of today. Former climates affected the amount of runoff during excavation. Previous landscape features also influenced how and where the Colorado River once flowed. These variables make it hard to understand how the modern Grand Canyon developed. In trying to discover the origin of such a large landscape, geologists are like the proverbial six blind men and the elephant—they touch and feel a small part of the beast but are misled into thinking they can describe it in its entirety.

Most geologists agree that it is only during the last 5 to 6 million years that the Grand Canyon has been cut to the great depth we see today. This time includes the last great Ice Age when large volumes of glacial meltwater from the Rockies likely increased the erosional power of the Colorado River. Additionally, faulting in the western part of the Canyon may have also enhanced the cutting power of the Colorado River in a process known as base level lowering. By lowering the river's channel in the west, it caused the river gradient in the eastern Canyon to steepen and progressively deepen. Multiple processes have likely worked hand-in-hand to create the Grand Canyon.

NPS PHOTO

THE GRAND CANYON

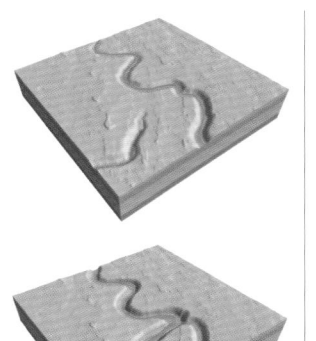

Many geologists believe that two separate and distinct river systems were somehow integrated to become the modern Colorado River. Three processes have been proposed for this integration:

• **Stream piracy** involves the progressive upstream lengthening of one drainage such that it intersects and captures flow from another (a bottom-up process).

• **Basin spillover** results from the sequential filling of ancient lakes that overflow their lowest rims, thus linking once separate basins (a top-down process).

• **Karst collapse** entails an initial subsurface integration by groundwater flow through confined caves that ultimately collapse and create a surface connection (a subterranean-to-surface process).

Stream piracy has historically been the most accepted explanation for the integration of two river systems. Some geologists however, prefer the theory that no integration event occurred; rather, they say the initial northeast drainage was reversed in its original channel by back-tilting of the larger Colorado Plateau landscape.

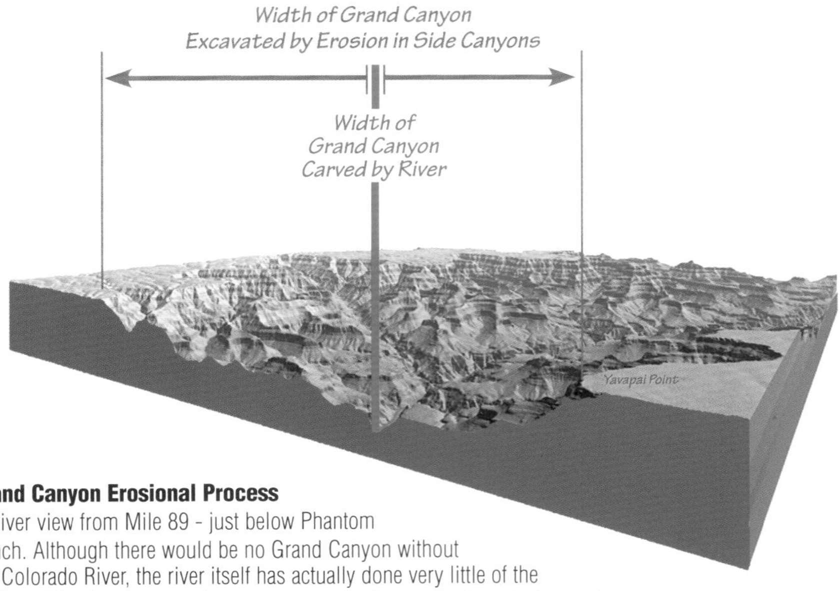

Stream Piracy occurs when a stream or river is diverted from its own bed, and flows instead down the bed of a neighboring stream.

Width of Grand Canyon Excavated by Erosion in Side Canyons

Width of Grand Canyon Carved by River

Yavapai Point

Grand Canyon Erosional Process
Upriver view from Mile 89 - just below Phantom Ranch. Although there would be no Grand Canyon without the Colorado River, the river itself has actually done very little of the cutting. Other forces of erosion such as gravity, freeze and thaw cycles, and side canyon dissection have made the canyon much wider than the river.

The Lavas

Lava Falls Rapid
was formed by rocky
debris coming out of
Prospect Canyon.

Volcanic showcase.
Computer enhanced
image of Lava Falls
region shows spectacular
lava flows that poured
into the Grand Canyon
between 830,000 to
100,000 years ago.
Ancient lava dam and
reservoir have been
superimposed on image.

A nother set of rocks is sporadically but dramatically exposed between river miles 179 and 255. These are basalt lava flows that erupted above and within the Canyon, beginning about 830,000 years ago. These voluminous lava flows sometimes dammed the Colorado River creating large temporary reservoirs. Up to thirteen dams were formed, some of which were hundreds to thousands of feet high. They were inherently unstable however, as they formed on top of loose river gravel, or because the lava shattered upon contact with river water. Certain deposits show that on at least five different occasions these lava dams failed catastrophically in huge outburst flood events. Although the lavas are silent today, their history is evident on the Canyon walls.

As you travel down the river, look up from the great depths and imagine all of the time and the great sequence of events that acted in concert to create this landscape masterpiece.

IMAGE COMPOSITE: BUZZ BELKNAP   SOURCES: USDA-NAIP IMAGE, USGS GCMRC IMAGE, & USGS QUAD DEM

GEOLOGY

HOW IT HAPPENED

The major geologic events leading to the formation of the Grand Canyon are shown in these illustrations. All time periods are approximations.

Note: *Unconformities* are missing chapters in the geologic record that occur when erosion removes layers of rock. New layers are then deposited on top, creating a time gap in the geologic record. In the Canyon, the Great Unconformity and the Greatest Angular Unconformity are two major examples of this process.

Step 1 – *2,000 to 1,750 million years ago.* Sand, mud and lava accumulate to a great thickness as volcanic islands collide with the southern edge of ancient North America.

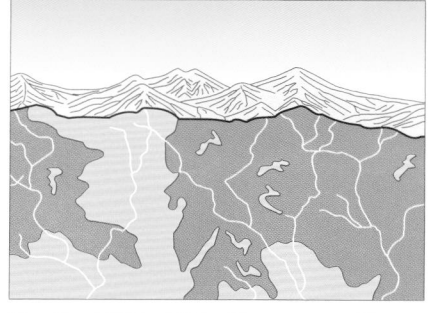

Step 2 – *1,750 to 1,254 million years ago.* These deposits are folded, buried, and metamorphosed into crystalline rocks, which are gradually brought back to the surface where an undulating plain forms across the landscape.

Step 3 – *1,254 to 740 million years ago.* Deposition of over 12,000 feet of sediment and lava, the Grand Canyon Supergroup, on top of the eroded mountains, creating the Greatest Angular Unconformity (marked by red line).

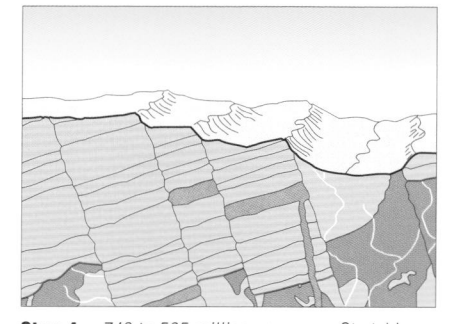

Step 4 – *740 to 505 million years ago.* Stretching of the earth's crust creates faults and tilts the Supergroup rocks down to the northeast. Most of the package is removed by erosion and only wedge-shaped remnants remain.

Step 5 – *505 million years ago.* An ancient sea slowly inundates the eroded surface and creates the Great Unconformity (blue line above). The Tapeats Sandstone rests immediately above this gap in the rock record.

Step 6 – *505 to 270 million years ago.* Throughout most of the Paleozoic Era (some 235 million years of time) many different layers of sediment accumulated and hardened into the strata that enclose the Grand Canyon. (Paleozoic/Mesozoic unconformity marked as green line above).

Step 7 – *252 to 66 million years ago.* Mesozoic-age deposits cover the Grand Canyon region with up to 10,000 feet of additional rock strata. These deposits are mostly eroded now except for remnants at the Vermilion and Echo cliffs near Lees Ferry.

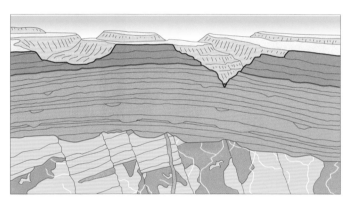

Step 8 – *70 to 25 million years ago.* Uplift of the Rocky Mountains and the Colorado Plateau places all of these rock units into a position where they are subject to erosion. An initial northeast drainage pattern forms on the landscape.

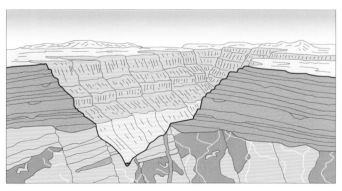

Step 9 – *25 million years ago to present.* The Basin and Range Disturbance lowers the landscape west of Grand Canyon. By 6 million years ago the river system flowed towards the newly created Gulf of California. Grand Canyon is deepened and widened at this time.

GEOLOGY

ROCK SEQUENCE

The sequence below shows successive rock layers in the Grand Canyon
from oldest at the bottom to youngest at the top.

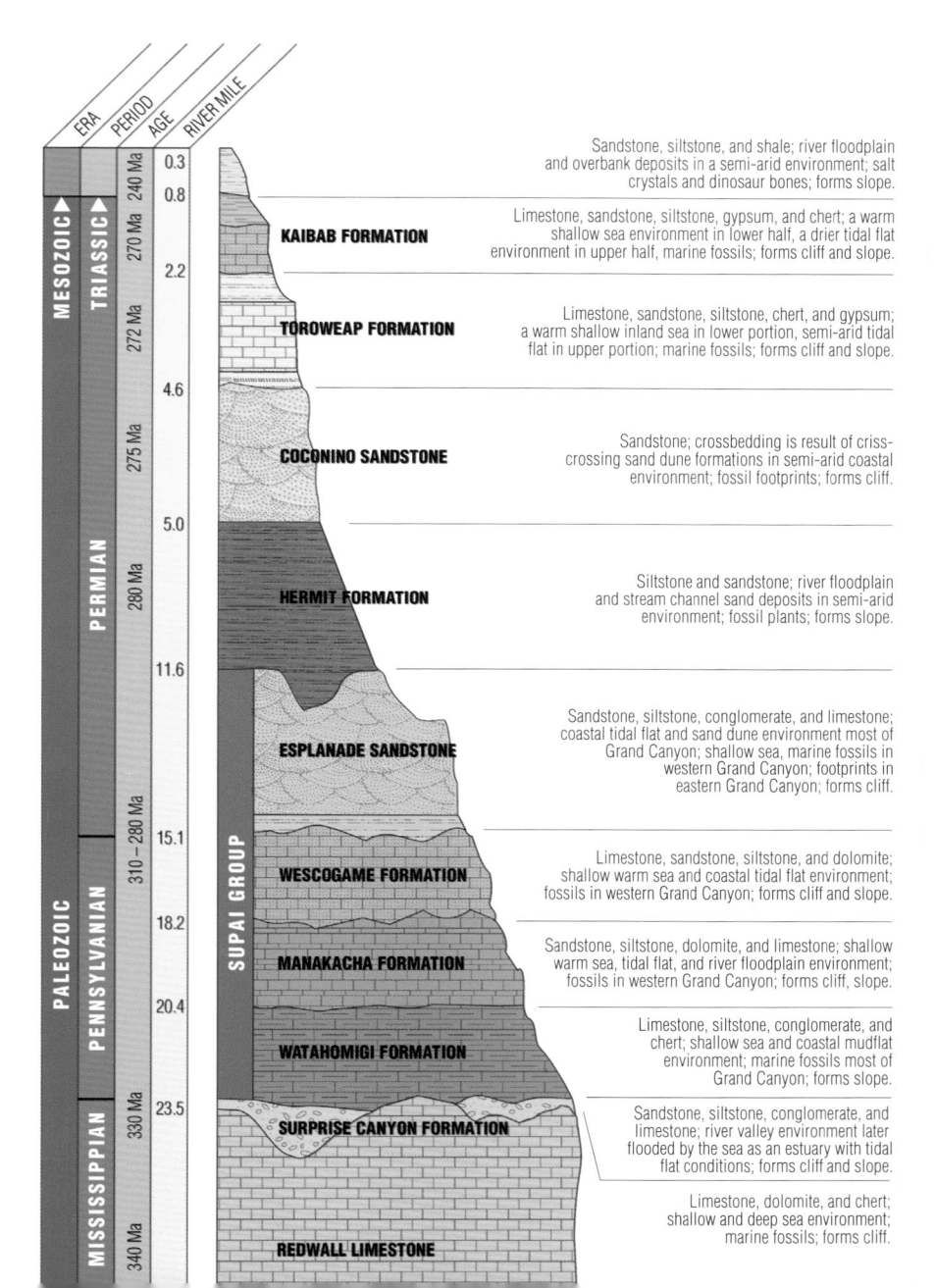

Sandstone, siltstone, and shale; river floodplain and overbank deposits in a semi-arid environment; salt crystals and dinosaur bones; forms slope.

KAIBAB FORMATION — Limestone, sandstone, siltstone, gypsum, and chert; a warm shallow sea environment in lower half, a drier tidal flat environment in upper half, marine fossils; forms cliff and slope.

TOROWEAP FORMATION — Limestone, sandstone, siltstone, chert, and gypsum; a warm shallow inland sea in lower portion, semi-arid tidal flat in upper portion; marine fossils; forms cliff and slope.

COCONINO SANDSTONE — Sandstone; crossbedding is result of criss-crossing sand dune formations in semi-arid coastal environment; fossil footprints; forms cliff.

HERMIT FORMATION — Siltstone and sandstone; river floodplain and stream channel sand deposits in semi-arid environment; fossil plants; forms slope.

ESPLANADE SANDSTONE — Sandstone, siltstone, conglomerate, and limestone; coastal tidal flat and sand dune environment most of Grand Canyon; shallow sea, marine fossils in western Grand Canyon; footprints in eastern Grand Canyon; forms cliff.

WESCOGAME FORMATION — Limestone, sandstone, siltstone, and dolomite; shallow warm sea and coastal tidal flat environment; fossils in western Grand Canyon; forms cliff and slope.

MANAKACHA FORMATION — Sandstone, siltstone, dolomite, and limestone; shallow warm sea, tidal flat, and river floodplain environment; fossils in western Grand Canyon; forms cliff, slope.

WATAHOMIGI FORMATION — Limestone, siltstone, conglomerate, and chert; shallow sea and coastal mudflat environment; marine fossils most of Grand Canyon; forms slope.

SURPRISE CANYON FORMATION — Sandstone, siltstone, conglomerate, and limestone; river valley environment later flooded by the sea as an estuary with tidal flat conditions; forms cliff and slope.

REDWALL LIMESTONE — Limestone, dolomite, and chert; shallow and deep sea environment; marine fossils; forms cliff.

(Left axis labels: ERA, PERIOD, AGE, RIVER MILE)

MESOZOIC — **TRIASSIC** — 240 Ma — 0.3, 0.8

270 Ma — 2.2

272 Ma

275 Ma — 4.6

PALEOZOIC — **PERMIAN** — 280 Ma — 5.0

11.6

SUPAI GROUP — 310 – 280 Ma — 15.1, 18.2, 20.4, 23.5

PENNSYLVANIAN

MISSISSIPPIAN — 330 Ma, 340 Ma

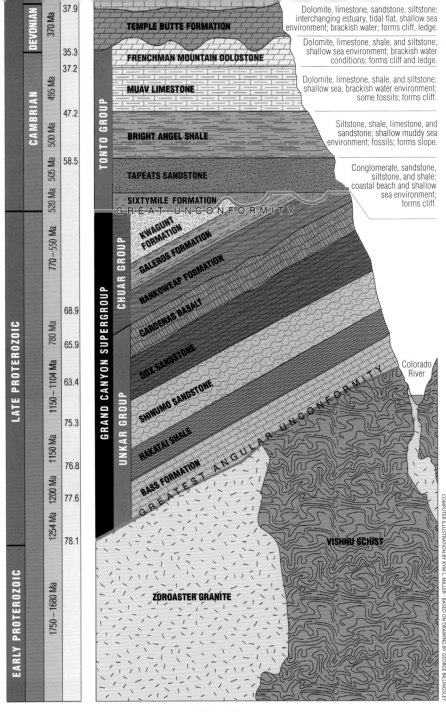

DEVONIAN

370 Ma

37.9

TEMPLE BUTTE FORMATION

Dolomite, limestone, sandstone, siltstone; interchanging estuary, tidal flat, shallow sea environment; brackish water; forms cliff, ledge.

35.3

FRENCHMAN MOUNTAIN DOLOSTONE

Dolomite, limestone, shale, and siltstone; shallow sea environment; brackish water conditions; forms cliff and ledge.

37.2

CAMBRIAN

495 Ma

MUAV LIMESTONE

Dolomite, limestone, shale, and siltstone; shallow sea, brackish water environment; some fossils; forms cliff.

47.2

500 Ma

BRIGHT ANGEL SHALE

Siltstone, shale, limestone, and sandstone; shallow muddy sea environment; fossils; forms slope.

58.5

505 Ma

TONTO GROUP

TAPEATS SANDSTONE

Conglomerate, sandstone, siltstone, and shale; coastal beach and shallow sea environment; forms cliff.

520 Ma

SIXTYMILE FORMATION

G R E A T   U N C O N F O R M I T Y

LATE PROTEROZOIC

770 – 550 Ma

KWAGUNT FORMATION

GALEROS FORMATION

NANKOWEAP FORMATION

CHUAR GROUP

CARDENAS BASALT

68.9

780 Ma

DOX SANDSTONE

65.9

1150 – 1104 Ma

SHINUMO SANDSTONE

63.4

Colorado River

GRAND CANYON SUPERGROUP

75.3

1150 Ma

HAKATAI SHALE

UNKAR GROUP

76.8

1200 Ma

BASS FORMATION

77.6

1254 Ma

G R E A T E S T   A N G U L A R   U N C O N F O R M I T Y

78.1

EARLY PROTEROZOIC

1750 – 1680 Ma

ZOROASTER GRANITE

VISHNU SCHIST

COMPUTER ILLUSTRATION BY KYM L. MILLER · BASED ON DRAWING BY GEORGE BILLINGSLEY

FOR GRAND CANYON GEOLOGY ROCK SEQUENCE POSTER, VISIT WWW.WESTWATERBOOKS.COM

GEOLOGY

PHOTO GUIDE TO CANYON ROCK FORMATIONS

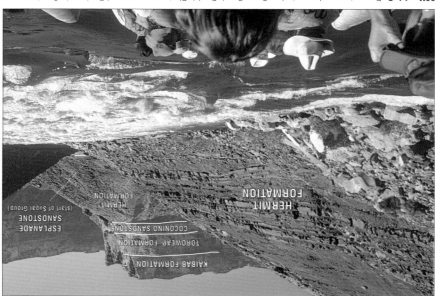

FORMATION LABELING BY GEORGE BILLINGSLEY

LOIE BELKNAP EVANS

Mile 4.9 Upstream view of Navajo Bridges, spanning the Canyon some 470 feet above the river. First appearance of Coconino Sandstone at river level (Mile 4.6).

BILL BELKNAP

Mile 11.2 Downstream view entering Soap Creek Rapid. First appearance of Esplanade Sandstone at foot of rapid (Mile 11.6). Rim is 1,170 feet above the river.

Mile 18.6 Upstream view. Manakacha Formation appears at Mile 18.2. Rim is 1,855 feet above river.

BUZZ BELKNAP

KAIBAB FORMATION

TOROWEAP FORMATION

COCONINO SANDSTONE

HERMIT FORMATION

SUPAI GROUP

REDWALL LIMESTONE

TEMPLE BUTTE FORMATION

FRENCHMAN MOUNTAIN DOLOSTONE

MUAV LIMESTONE

BRIGHT ANGEL SHALE (covered)

Mile 52.3 Downstream view at head of Nankoweap Rapid. Rim is 3,200 feet above the river.

GEOLOGY

BUZZ BELKNAP

KAIBAB FORMATION
TOROWEAP FORMATION
COCONINO SANDSTONE
ESPLANADE SANDSTONE
WESCOGAME FORMATION
MANAKACHA FORMATION
WATAHOMIGI FORMATION
SUPAI GROUP
REDWALL LIMESTONE
TEMPLE BUTTE FORMATION
FRENCHMAN MOUNTAIN DOLOSTONE
REDWALL LIMESTONE
TEMPLE BUTTE FORMATION
FRENCHMAN MOUNTAIN DOLOSTONE
talus
MUAV LIMESTONE
MUAV LIMESTONE
BRIGHT ANGEL SHALE
transition zone
TAPEATS SANDSTONE

Mile 61.9 Downstream view from mouth of Little Colorado River to Chuar Butte. Note full exposure of Paleozoic sequence from Kaibab Formation to Tapeats Sandstone (Hermit Formation obscured from view). Rim is 3,760 feet above the river.

SHINUMO
SANDSTONE

HAKATAI
SHALE

Hance
Asbestos Mine

BASS FORMATION

diabase sill

VISHNU SCHIST

BASS Fm

GREATEST ANGULAR
UNCONFORMITY

Mile 77.1 Downstream view, entering Hance Rapid. Formations visible (other than Vishnu Schist) are part of Grand Canyon Supergroup. South Rim at far left is 4,700 feet above the river level.

KAIBAB FORMATION
TOROWEAP FORMATION
COCONINO SANDSTONE
HERMIT FORMATION
SUPAI GROUP   TAPEATS SANDSTONE
(about 525 million years old)

THE GREAT UNCONFORMITY
(about a 1,200 million year break in rock record)

VISHNU SCHIST (black)
&
ZOROASTER GRANITE (pink)

(about 1.7 to 1.66 billion years old)

Mile 82.6 Upstream view typical of the Inner Gorge.

GEOLOGY

GEOLOGY

PHOTO GUIDE TO CANYON ROCK FORMATIONS
2017 – New Photo Section below Phantom, by Brad Dimock & George Billingsley

Mile 108.5 Downstream aerial view, Shinumo area. The Grand Canyon Supergroup reappears from Mile 107 to 111, sandwiched at an angle between the Paleozoic rocks above and the pre-cambrian schists and granites below.

Mile 121 Downstream view. In Conquistador Aisle only the Paleozoic sequence is exposed. Rusty brown dolomite layers begin appearing in the Bright Angel Shale.

Mile 131 Downstream view. Below Bedrock Rapid the Supergroup returns once again. Half a billion years ago the advancing sea draped Tapeats Sandstone and Bright Angel Shale upon the shores of Shinumo Sandstone Islands.

Mile 155 Downstream view just above Supai. The western reaches of Grand Canyon, closer to the ocean, received more limestone deposits and experienced less erosion. Temple Butte and the Frenchman Mountain Dolostone thicken dramatically.

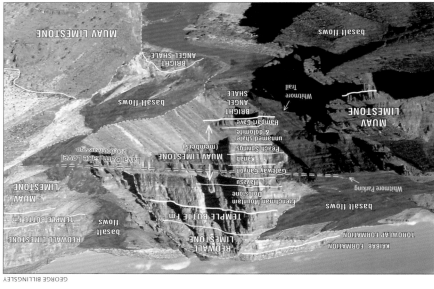

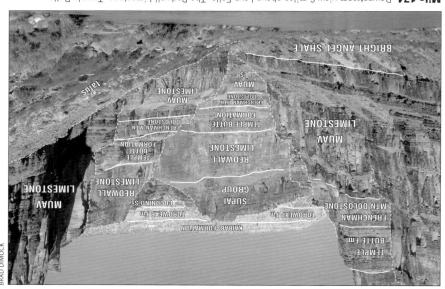

2017 – New Photo Section below Phantom, by Brad Dimock & George Billingsley

BRAD DIMOCK

Mile 174 Downstream view 6 miles above Lava Falls. The Redwall Limestone, Temple Butte Formation, Frenchman Mountain Dolostone, and Muav Limestone, similar in composition, become increasingly difficult to tell apart.

Labels in upper photo (img_2):
BRIGHT ANGEL SHALE
MUAV LIMESTONE
MUAV Ls
talus
FRENCHMAN MTN DOLOSTONE
TEMPLE BUTTE FORMATION
REDWALL LIMESTONE
TEMPLE BUTTE FORMATION
MUAV LIMESTONE
FRENCHMAN MTN DOLOSTONE
SUPAI GROUP
TOROWEAP Fm
COCONINO SS.
KAIBAB FORMATION
TOROWEAP Fm
REDWALL LIMESTONE
FRENCHMAN MTN DOLOSTONE
TEMPLE BUTTE Fm

GEORGE BILLINGSLEY

Mile 188 Upstream aerial view below Whitmore Wash. In the last million years multiple flows of lava poured into the river between Lava Falls and Whitmore Wash, damming the river multiple times and flowing over 70 miles down the river channel.

Labels in lower photo (img_1):
MUAV LIMESTONE
BRIGHT ANGEL SHALE
basalt flows
MUAV LIMESTONE
basalt flows
BRIGHT ANGEL SHALE
Whitmore Trail
Rampart Cave
unnamed shale & dolomite (members)
Peach Springs
Kanab
Gateway Canyon
Lava Dam Lake Level 200,000 years ago
MUAV LIMESTONE
Havasu
Frenchman Mountain Dolostone
Whitmore Parking
MUAV LIMESTONE
TEMPLE BUTTE Fm
TEMPLE BUTTE Fm
basalt flows
REDWALL LIMESTONE
REDWALL LIMESTONE
basalt flows
TOROWEAP FORMATION
KAIBAB FORMATION

PAKOON LIMESTONE
ESPLANADE Ss
SUPAI GROUP

PAKOON LIMESTONE   ESPLANADE Ss

REDWALL LIMESTONE

SUPAI GROUP

TEMPLE BUTTE Fm

FRENCHMAN MOUNTAIN DOLOSTONE

MUAV LIMESTONE

Lake Mead silt banks

Mile 274 Downstream view last bend in Canyon. Near the canyon's western margin the limestones and dolomites achieve an astounding thickness, dwarfing the upper formations.

Snap Point
Kaibab overlain by Lava

Colorado River exits Grand Canyon

G r a n d   W a s h   C l i f f s

Lake Mead sill

MIOCENE CONGLOMERATE

MIOCENE CONGLOMERATE

Pearce Ferry Rapid

Un-runnable Pearce Ferry Rapid formed in 2001 where muck-mired river missed former channel. For full details see Map 45.

Mile 279.8 Looking east toward the end of Grand Canyon. At Pearce Ferry one can gaze back at Grand Wash Cliffs, where Grand Canyon and the Colorado plateau end abruptly at the Grand Wash Fault. Snap Point provides the last glimpse of Kaibab Limestone, the Canyon's true rim.

CHARLY HEAVENRICH

JUSTIN HOWE

Why should your boatman have all the fun?

River running has come a long way since John Wesley Powell's day when his crew sat with their backs to oncoming rapids while rowing heavy wooden boats downstream. In 1896, after trapper Nathaniel Galloway worked out a stern-first, face-forward rowing style that allowed greater maneuverability, whitewater boating techniques improved considerably. Today river running is a well-developed art and science. A skilled river guide has many choices that Powell and his men did not. Knowledge of river currents, coupled with highly developed rowing or motoring skills, allow precision river running. For instance, choosing a conservative course may keep the passengers dry, but opting for a more daring run adds excitement and the possibility of a drenching spray.

Rating rapids according to difficulty can be a useful tool. It's important to understand that ratings are relative. They're dependent on water level, a boatman's ability, and boat type and size. Deciphering river jargon can be puzzling at first. It helps take the mystery out of river running if first-timers understand fastwater basics and know common terms used by boatmen such as *hole, sleeper, tongue, eddy,* and *c.f.s.* The diagrams and section below explain these terms.

Scouting a rapid

Hole: Churning water downstream from submerged rock.

Tongue: V-shaped smooth water at head of rapid.

Sleeper: Smooth "pillow" of water hiding a shallow rock.

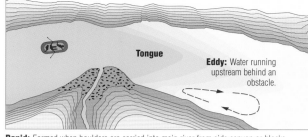

Tongue

Eddy: Water running upstream behind an obstacle.

Rapid: Formed when boulders are carried into main river from side canyon or blocks tumble from cliffs, obstructing river and making it narrower and faster.

Side view of above

"I've been wondering ..."

How deep is the river?

Depth varies from inches to about one hundred feet. The most striking feature about river depth is how suddenly it may change. Many have taken an involuntary swim by misjudging the depth.

How wide?

Width ranges from 76 feet at Granite Narrows, Mile 136, to about 750 feet at Mile 193. The average width is 200-300 feet.

How cold?

Water released from Glen Canyon Dam is about 46 degrees F., warming to approximately 50 degrees at Phantom Ranch, 60 degrees at Lake Mead. Winter temperatures are slightly colder.

How fast?

The river may reach speeds of 10-15 m.p.h. at steeper rapids. Average smooth water speed is 3-4 m.p.h. Drop in elevation and volume of water influence speed.

How far does it drop?

It drops a total of 1,709 feet in the 296 miles covered by this Guide, averaging approximately 8 feet per mile— nearly 25 times that of the Mississippi River.

What is c.f.s.?

Recent tree ring studies reveal periods of drought and flood which pre-date gaging records.

River flow is measured in c.f.s., or cubic feet per second. This is the number of cubic feet of water passing a particular point at a given second. The lowest documented flow since the construction of Glen Canyon Dam is 1,000 c.f.s., measured in 1977; the highest 97,262 c.f.s. in 1983. Pre-dam highs may have exceeded 240,000 c.f.s. in the 1800s, and 300,000 c.f.s. in the 400s to 800s though flows weren't accurately measured until 1922.

WHITEWATER WORKSHOP

HIGHS, LOWS, AND RIVER FLOWS

ALLEN GILBERG

River running is dramatically affected by daily fluctuations in water released from Glen Canyon Dam in response to changing demands for hydro-electric power in the West. The amount of water flowing through the turbines determines how much electricity is generated to meet those demands. Peak flows coincide with peak energy needs. Information about daily flows is available from the Bureau of Reclamation at Page, Arizona, or from the ranger at Lees Ferry.

The National Park Service regulates river travel through Grand Canyon. The Colorado River Management Plan (CRMP) released in March of 2006 is a visitor use plan which specifies actions to help conserve park resources while enhancing recreational opportunities and the visitor experience. Details on the CRMP and accompanying Environmental Impact Statements are available on the NPS website.

Concessions have been issued to sixteen qualified commercial outfitters who are authorized to offer river trips of varying lengths to the public in a variety of boat types. Some commercial outfitters also offer provision and logistical support for do-it-yourself boaters

About half of present-day river use is by private or non-commercial groups. Currently a lottery system is in place to obtain a non-commercial permit.

A five and one-half month period in the summer season allows for both motorized and non-motorized trips with the rest of the year being reserved for rowing and paddling trips only.

Push comes to shove when changing power demands create daily fluctuations in river level.

River Flow Hotline Call 800-752-8525 for daily flow releases from Glen Canyon Dam, or visit www.usbr.gov/uc/water/crsp/cs/gcd.html

The National Park Service is the regulatory agency for Grand Canyon National Park. For up-to-date information on boating, camping and important regulations visit their website at: www.nps.gov/grca/ or call 928-638-7888

NPS PHOTO BY MARK LELLOUCH

Havasupai Tribe:
www.havasupai-nsn.gov
928-448-2121 for all
reservations: hiking,
camping, lodging

Hualapai Tribe:
www.grandcanyonwest.com
928-769-2219

**Common
Canyon craft**
include dories, kayaks,
oar-powered rafts, and
motorized pontoons.

For up-to-date information on both commercial and non-commercial river trips, camping information, Park Service regulations, and safety requirements call the River Permits Office toll free: 800-959-9164 or visit the Park website at www.nps.gov/grca/.

For additional information on river trips between Diamond Creek and Lake Mead and Tribal land fees, contact the Hualapai Tribe at 928-769-2219 or 800-622-4409.

Boaters wishing to hike upstream beyond Beaver Falls on tribal lands at Havasu must get a permit from the Havasupai Tribe. Call 928-448-2121.

ALLEN GILBERG

ALLEN GILBERG

ALLEN GILBERG

ARIZONA RAFT ADVENTURES

THE GREAT UNKNOWN

"The Grand Canyon discovered in 1540 by Pedro de Cardenas" the National Parks pamphlet read I smiled knowing that my people always knew the Grand Canyon was there and didn't need to be discovered.

Michael Kabotie (Lomawywesa)
Hopi artist and poet

From a poem entitled *"Grand Canyon National Park,"* published in *Migration Tears, Poems About Transitions,* American Indian Studies Center, UCLA, 1987

MARSTON COLLECTION

Major John Wesley Powell and his exploratory expedition left Green River, Wyoming, on May 24, 1869, for a journey into "…the Great Unknown."

U.S. Postage Stamp commemorated the Powell Expedition in 1969.

Archaeologic evidence now suggests that parts of the Grand Canyon have been occupied intermittently by Native Americans for more than 10,000 years. The first non-native peoples to observe the Grand Canyon were Spanish soldiers led by Captain Garcia Lopez de Cardenas who arrived at the South Rim with Hopi guides in 1540. Their exploratory mission was part of the search for the fabled Seven Cities of Gold under the direction of Francisco Vasquez de Coronado.

In 1869, Major John Wesley Powell, a Civil War veteran who had lost his right arm in the Battle of Shiloh, led the first voyage to explore the Grand Canyon.

Until then the Canyon appeared on maps of the West as a mysterious void. Streams ran into it and the Colorado River flowed out, but before Powell, no one had the scientific curiosity or the courage to go down it. In Grand Canyon, three of his men left before the trip was over (see Map 39). They climbed to the rim hoping to reach a Mormon outpost. They never arrived.

About 100 people
had traveled by boat through the Grand Canyon by 1949–eighty years after Powell's voyage. Approximately 27,000 each year now repeat his journey into "The Great Unknown."

Georgie White Clark
a Grand Canyon legend, popularized pontoons for commercial boating, ran her own trips for more than forty years.

Georgie's G-rig,
the start of something big.

Powell concluded they were killed by Indians. On August 29, 1869, Powell's gaunt crew rowed out of the Grand Canyon into open country 65 miles from the settlement of Las Vegas, Nevada.

Powell's feat did not trigger a burst of activity in the Grand Canyon. A determined few followed from time to time—prospectors, trappers, geologists, and mapmakers. Robert Brewster Stanton hoped to build a railroad; the brothers Emery and Ellsworth Kolb made a film. In 1923 the U.S. Geological Survey conducted the first and only instrument survey of the Colorado River through Grand Canyon. One couple, Glen and Bessie Hyde, nearly completed the journey in a sweepscow before they vanished. Buzz Holmstrom built his own boat and made the trip alone. Botanists Dr. Elzada Clover and Lois Jotter became the first women to successfully complete a Canyon run, traveling with Norman Nevills in 1938. Nevills later began taking passengers for hire. But by 1949—eighty years after Powell—about 100 people had traveled through the Grand Canyon.

Ed Hudson and Dock Marston drove the first powerboat, *Esmeralda II*, through in 1949, setting a record of four and one-half days. Two years later Jim and Bob Rigg rowed through in two and one-half days. That same year Jimmy Jordan and Rod Sanderson ran the Canyon using outboard motors for the first time.

When war surplus inflatable craft became available, Georgie White Clark pioneered present-day commercial river running. Lashing three war surplus bridge pontoons side by side and steering them with an outboard motor, she packed aboard up to 30 passengers. Others began building versions of the G-rig, as they called Georgie's creation.

In 1960 the only successful uprun of the Grand Canyon was made in jet boats.

A CONCERN FOR ECOLOGY

Intrepid crew of 1923 U.S. Geological Survey, led by Claude Birdseye, (fourth from left) completed first and only instrument survey of the Colorado River through Grand Canyon. The USGS Plan and Profile maps created as a result became the basis for the first Belknap *Grand Canyon River Guide,* the Powell Centennial Edition, published in 1969.

USGS COLLECTION

In 1963 an important chapter of Grand Canyon history was closed when natural flows of the Colorado River were halted and replaced with daily energy-related releases from Glen Canyon Dam. The controversial dam and the reservoir behind it, Lake Powell, became a springboard for environmental activism.

Dams were proposed within the Canyon itself as early as 1913. Numerous potential sites were identified by the 1923 USGS Expedition. Investigations continued for years, but it was not until the 1960s that the country's growing environmental movement began to seriously challenge the dam-builders. The prospect of a dam in the Canyon sparked a highly publicized fight between dam-builders and conservationists. Anti-dam forces prevailed; further flooding of the Canyon floor is unlikely.

21st Century Balancing Act: Optimizing man's management of the Colorado River

Striking a balance between the interests of river, rim, trail, and air visitors while protecting the environment, is of utmost importance today. For example, in response to pressure from noise-conscious hikers and boaters and public concern about air safety in the river corridor, Congress in 1988 enacted legislation creating flight-free air zones over the Canyon.

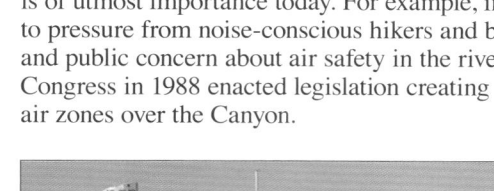

Ford Tri-motor over the Canyon, 1930s. Scenic flights remain one of the most popular ways to view the Canyon.

BILL BELKNAP

Teddy Roosevelt
and John Hance at South Rim in 1903.Roosevelt proclaimed Grand Canyon a National Monument in 1908 under the Antiquities Act established in 1906. It became a National Park in 1919.

" . . . the Grand Canyon . . . . Leave it as it is. You cannot improve on it. The ages have been at work on it, and man can only mar it."
Teddy Roosevelt

NOTE:
The Adaptive Management Program, which will continue under the LTEMP (Long-Term Environmental Management Program). Record of Decision(ROD), December 2016, still includes some beach-building High-Flow Experiments (HFE)
www.usbr.gov/uc/rm/amp/index.html

Glen Canyon Dam

GLEN CANYON ENVIRONMENTAL STUDIES

In 1982 the Bureau of Reclamation set up Glen Canyon Environmental Studies, a program that addressed ecological concerns about the impact of Glen Canyon Dam on the river environment. Discoveries under the program led to the Grand Canyon Protection Act of 1992 (GCPA), a federal law mandating the establishment of protective policies in the river corridor.

The Glen Canyon Dam Adaptive Management Program in use today is an initiative resulting from passage of the GCPA, its ensuing Environmental Statement of 1996, and now the 2016 Long-Term Environmental Management Plan—LTEMP—intended to provide a framework for continued adaptive management of Glen Canyon Dam over the next 20 years. The plan includes continued High-Flow Experiments when conditions allow, in order to move accumulated sediment downstream to help replace once plentiful sandy beaches—the most recent test flow was in November 2018. The Grand Canyon Monitoring and Research Center (GCMRC) serves as the principal research and monitoring entity, working with partner bureaus and researchers to understand and predict the relationship between Glen Canyon Dam operations and downstream resources—natural, recreational, ecological, and cultural. The information is used by the Department of Interior managers in how best to operate Glen Canyon Dam to further the goals of the GCPA and the LTEMP.

The balancing act between man and nature continues. Although much has changed since 1869, each year enthusiastic river runners add their names to the annals of Grand Canyon history. But a trip down the river, into ". . . the Great Unknown" remains as much a unique and exciting adventure as it was in the days of Major John Wesley Powell.

RIVER MAPS

USING YOUR RIVER GUIDE

John Wesley Powell

Powell Report. This notation indicates condensed quotations from *Exploration of the Colorado River of the West and Its Tributaries Explored in 1869, 1870, 1871, and 1872* by John Wesley Powell, U.S. Government Printing Office, 1875.

Powell Report

True North

River Miles are based on the 2002 U.S. Geological Survey conducted by the Grand Canyon Monitoring and Research Center (GCMRC). Distances are measured along the river center line—with Mile 0 at Lees Ferry. Traveling upriver to Glen Canyon Dam, mileages go from *0 to -15*, and downriver to Pearce Ferry, from *0 to 280*.

125

Rapid ratings (numbers in parentheses) are given on a scale of 1 – 10, *with 10 the most difficult. Ratings are based on river flows of between 5,000 and 25,000 cubic feet per second (c.f.s.). Drops based on 1924 USGS Plan and Profile survey.*

Rapid (2–4)
Drop 7'

ALL NEW RIVER FLOW FORMAT Read-As-You-Run. River now flows from bottom to top of page. Large blue arrow indicates directional flow of river.

River Campsites in Grand Canyon from National Park Service (NPS) inventory database, give size designation based on number of people they can accomodate: **(XS)** Very Small: 1–6; **(S)** Small 7–12; **(M)** Medium 13–18; **(L)** Large 19–and above.

River Campsite (M)

Geologic faults are stress-caused displacement zones in Earth's crust; U (up), D (down), and numbers indicate direction and approximate displacement.

FAULT, 500'
U
D

Contours are lines of constant elevation. Contour interval is 50 feet. Heavy contour line is 200. Lines close together indicate steep walls.

3200
3600

River elevations are measured above sea level. Below 1,221 feet, Hoover Dam controls level of Lake Mead in the lower Grand Canyon.

2750

River maps based on U.S. Geological Survey *Plan and Profile of Colorado River, Lees Ferry, Arizona, to Black Canyon, Arizona–Nevada*, 1924 and current USGS seven and one-half minute series quadrangle maps, and USGS digital elevation models (DEM).

NOTE: River channels change frequently, sometimes within a few hours. Rocks, sandbars, or other obstructions may suddenly appear or wash away. Due to possible changes subsequent to publication or inadvertent errors in source material, **WESTWATER BOOKS** cannot be held responsible for inaccuracies or omissions in *Grand Canyon River Guide*.

⋏ ATTENTION BOATERS:

Campsites in this Guide are subject to changing river conditions stemming from Glen Canyon Dam's fluctuating outflows. Check current dam releases on Bureau of Reclamation website: www.usbr.gov or call their hotline for daily release reports: 928-645-3978

For Grand Canyon, check NPS website: www.nps.gov/grca/parkmgmt/riv_mgt.htm for latest information on campsite inventory and restrictions as well as recommended high water campsites during High-Flow Experiments (HFE)

More information available at Grand Canyon Monitoring and Research Center website: www.gcmrc.gov/dasa/default.aspx

Glen Canyon

Clear cold water, blue ribbon trout fishing, and multicolored canyon walls characterize this 15-mile stretch between Glen Canyon Dam and Lees Ferry. There is no private trip put-in at the Dam, but commercial half-day and all-day trips from the Dam to Lees Ferry are provided by the authorized Park Service concessionaire Wilderness River Adventures based in the town of Page, AZ: www.RiverAdventures.com

Lees Ferry boat ramp provides access for upstream travel for motor boaters and fishermen. Paddlers and rafters wishing to travel downriver from near the base of the Dam to Lees Ferry will need a tow or a lift from a power boat or consider using Wilderness River Adventures's backhaul service. There are six first-come, first-served campsites in this stretch, complete with grill pits and restrooms. All trash must be packed out. No private permit is required between Lees Ferry and Glen Canyon Dam. For current river flow information call Bureau of Reclamation at 928-645-3978.

For more information (camping, boating, fishing, etc.), contact the National Park Service, Glen Canyon National Recreation Area: www.nps.gov/glca/index.htm

Panoramic view of world-renowned Horseshoe Bend just downriver from Glen Canyon Dam. Visitor rim access—see Map 2.

Grand Canyon

Historic Lees Ferry lies between Glen and Marble canyons, and today thousands of people throughout the world remember it as the starting point of a highlight in their lives—a Grand Canyon River trip. For complete information about all Grand Canyon trips—private or commercial—consult the National Park Service website: www.nps.gov/grca/planyourvisit/whitewater-rafting.htm

Some 250 campsites marked in this Guide are those officially listed in an inventory compiled by the National Park Service. All camping must be below the historic high water zone.

The NPS (National Park Service) and the GCMRC (Grand Canyon Monitoring and Research Center) work together in an ongoing effort to monitor changes to campsites and protect sensitive park resources, including the old high water zone. For current information see: www.gcmrc.gov/dasa/default.aspx

For latest campsite information as well as a detailed list of special use, restrictions and closures, and high water camps during higher than normal releases, boaters should check the NPS website before trip departure: www.nps.gov/grca/parkmgmt/riv_mgt.htm

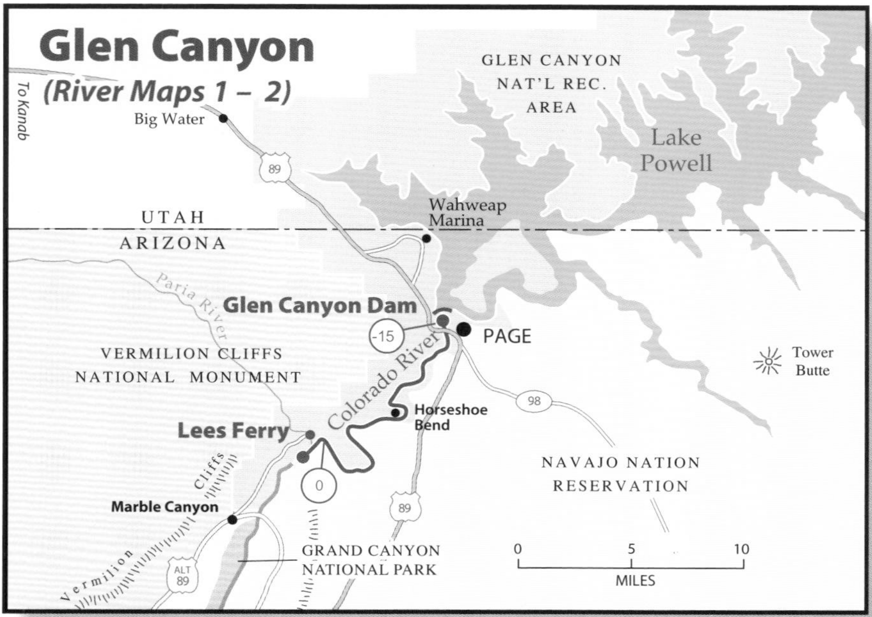

Glen Canyon
(River Maps 1 – 2)

To Kanab

Big Water

GLEN CANYON
NAT'L REC.
AREA

Lake
Powell

89

UTAH
ARIZONA

Wahweap
Marina

Paria River

Glen Canyon Dam

-15

PAGE

VERMILION CLIFFS
NATIONAL MONUMENT

Colorado River

Tower
Butte

Lees Ferry

Horseshoe
Bend

98

NAVAJO NATION
RESERVATION

Cliffs

0

Marble Canyon

89

0	5	10

MILES

Vermilion

ALT
89

GRAND CANYON
NATIONAL PARK

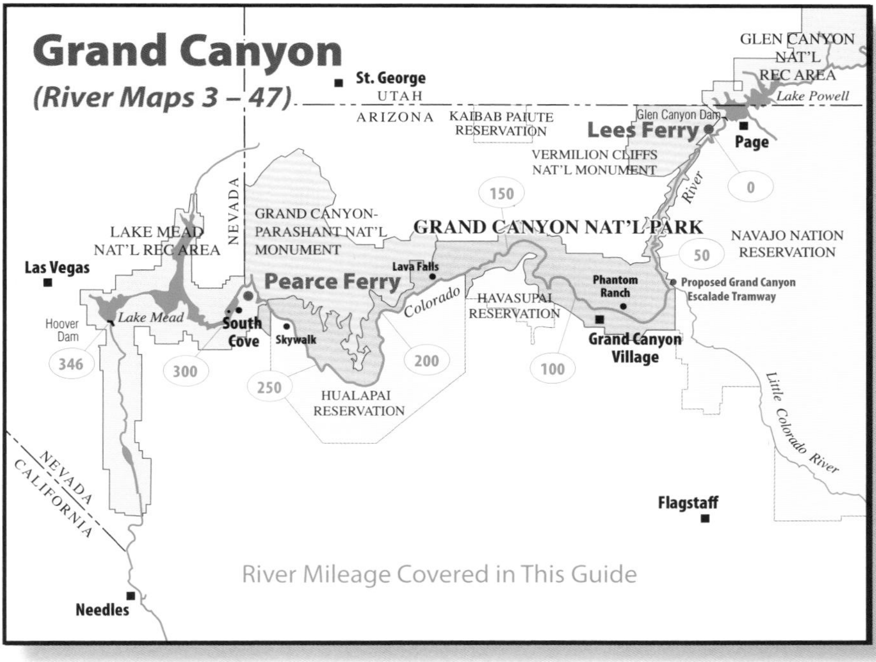

Grand Canyon
(River Maps 3 – 47)

St. George

GLEN CANYON
NAT'L
REC AREA

UTAH
ARIZONA

KAIBAB PAIUTE
RESERVATION

Lake Powell

Glen Canyon Dam

Lees Ferry

Page

VERMILION CLIFFS
NAT'L MONUMENT

150

River

0

NEVADA

GRAND CANYON-
PARASHANT NAT'L
MONUMENT

GRAND CANYON NAT'L PARK

NAVAJO NATION
RESERVATION

LAKE MEAD
NAT'L REC AREA

Lava Falls

50

Pearce Ferry

Phantom
Ranch

Proposed Grand Canyon
Escalade Tramway

Las Vegas

Colorado

HAVASUPAI
RESERVATION

Hoover
Dam

Lake Mead

**South
Cove**

Skywalk

200

100

**Grand Canyon
Village**

346

300

250

HUALAPAI
RESERVATION

Little Colorado River

NEVADA
CALIFORNIA

Flagstaff

River Mileage Covered in This Guide

Needles

Read-As-You-Run Format

Facing downstream, read map from bottom to top so that you can easily follow each river bend as you move downriver.

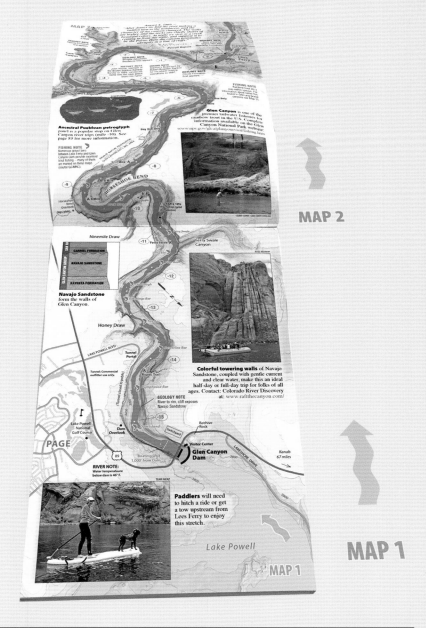

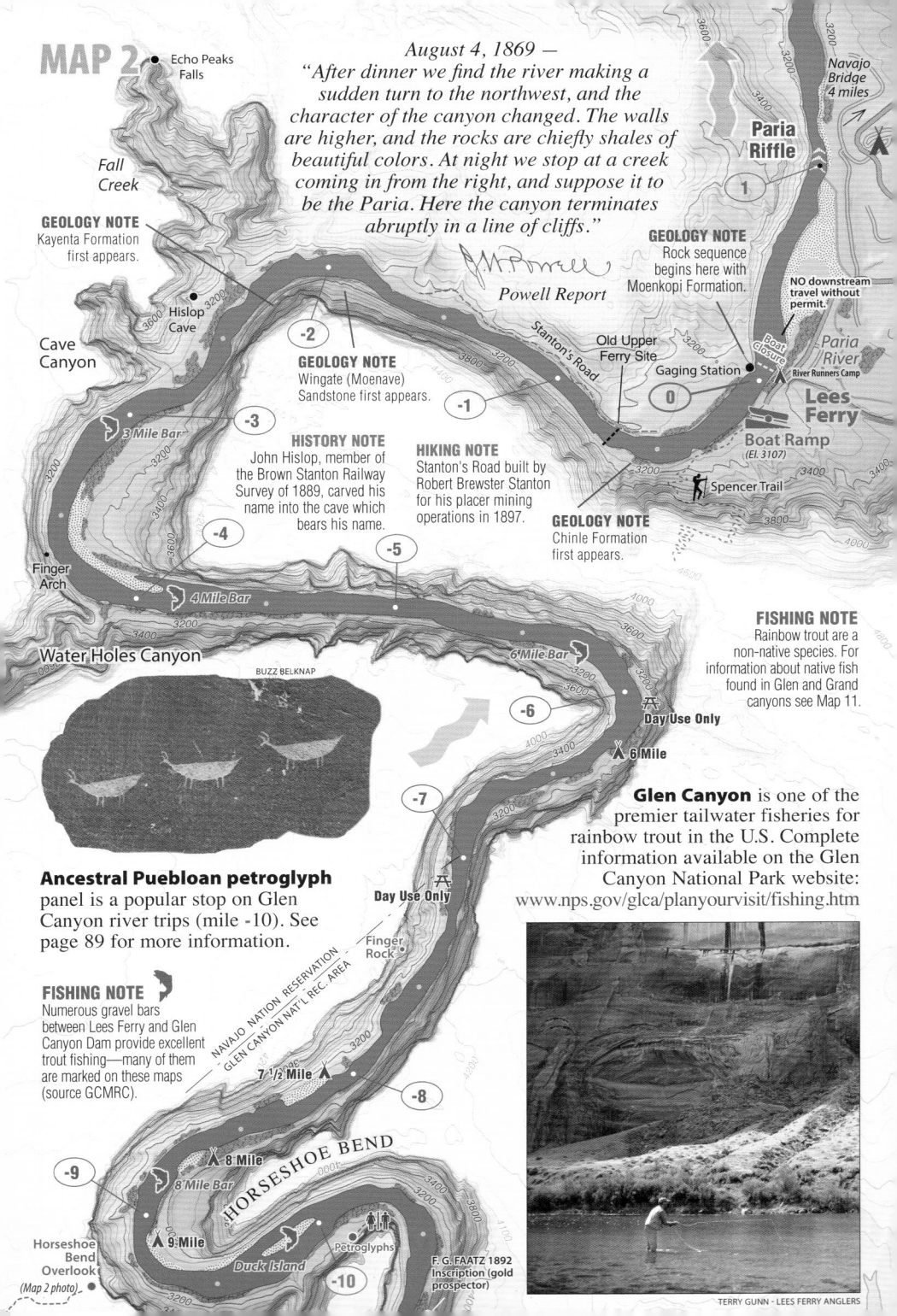

MAP 2

Echo Peaks Falls

August 4, 1869 —
"After dinner we find the river making a sudden turn to the northwest, and the character of the canyon changed. The walls are higher, and the rocks are chiefly shales of beautiful colors. At night we stop at a creek coming in from the right, and suppose it to be the Paria. Here the canyon terminates abruptly in a line of cliffs."

Powell Report

Navajo Bridge 4 miles

Paria Riffle

Fall Creek

GEOLOGY NOTE
Kayenta Formation first appears.

GEOLOGY NOTE
Rock sequence begins here with Moenkopi Formation.

NO downstream travel without permit.

Cave Canyon

Hislop Cave

Boat Closure

Paria River

River Runners Camp

Stanton's Road

Old Upper Ferry Site

Gaging Station

Lees Ferry

GEOLOGY NOTE
Wingate (Moenave) Sandstone first appears.

3 Mile Bar

Boat Ramp
(El. 3107)

HISTORY NOTE
John Hislop, member of the Brown Stanton Railway Survey of 1889, carved his name into the cave which bears his name.

HIKING NOTE
Stanton's Road built by Robert Brewster Stanton for his placer mining operations in 1897.

Spencer Trail

Finger Arch

GEOLOGY NOTE
Chinle Formation first appears.

4 Mile Bar

Water Holes Canyon

BUZZ BELKNAP

6 Mile Bar

Day Use Only

6 Mile

FISHING NOTE
Rainbow trout are a non-native species. For information about native fish found in Glen and Grand canyons see Map 11.

Glen Canyon is one of the premier tailwater fisheries for rainbow trout in the U.S. Complete information available on the Glen Canyon National Park website:
www.nps.gov/glca/planyourvisit/fishing.htm

Ancestral Puebloan petroglyph panel is a popular stop on Glen Canyon river trips (mile -10). See page 89 for more information.

Day Use Only

Finger Rock

FISHING NOTE
Numerous gravel bars between Lees Ferry and Glen Canyon Dam provide excellent trout fishing—many of them are marked on these maps (source GCMRC).

NAVAJO NATION RESERVATION
GLEN CANYON NAT'L REC. AREA

7 1/2 Mile

HORSESHOE BEND

8 Mile

8 Mile Bar

9 Mile

Horseshoe Bend Overlook
(Map 2 photo)

Duck Island

Petroglyphs

F. G. FAATZ 1892 Inscription (gold prospector)

TERRY GUNN - LEES FERRY ANGLERS

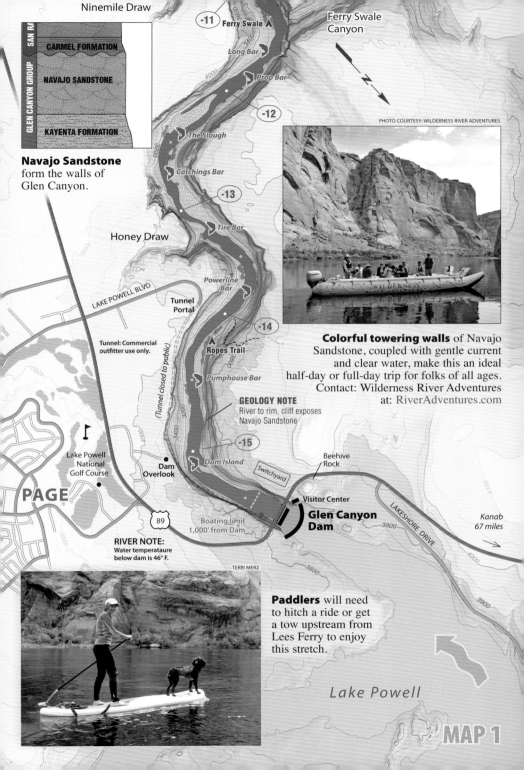

Ninemile Draw

-11 Ferry Swale

Ferry Swale Canyon

Long Bar

Prop Bar

-12

The Slough

Catchings Bar

-13

Tire Bar

Honey Draw

Powerline Bar

LAKE POWELL BLVD

Tunnel Portal

Tunnel: Commercial outfitter use only.

Ropes Trail

-14

Pumphouse Bar

(Tunnel closed to public)

GEOLOGY NOTE
River to rim, cliff exposes Navajo Sandstone

-15

Lake Powell National Golf Course

Dam Overlook

Dam Island

Switchyard

Beehive Rock

Visitor Center

Glen Canyon Dam

PAGE

89

Boating limit 1,000' from Dam

RIVER NOTE:
Water temperataure below dam is 46° F.

LAKESHORE DRIVE

Kanab 67 miles

3800

3800

3900

GLEN CANYON GROUP

SAN RA...
CARMEL FORMATION
NAVAJO SANDSTONE
KAYENTA FORMATION

Navajo Sandstone
form the walls of
Glen Canyon.

Colorful towering walls of Navajo
Sandstone, coupled with gentle current
and clear water, make this an ideal
half-day or full-day trip for folks of all ages.
Contact: Wilderness River Adventures
at: RiverAdventures.com

TERRI MERZ

Paddlers will need
to hitch a ride or get
a tow upstream from
Lees Ferry to enjoy
this stretch.

Lake Powell

MAP 1

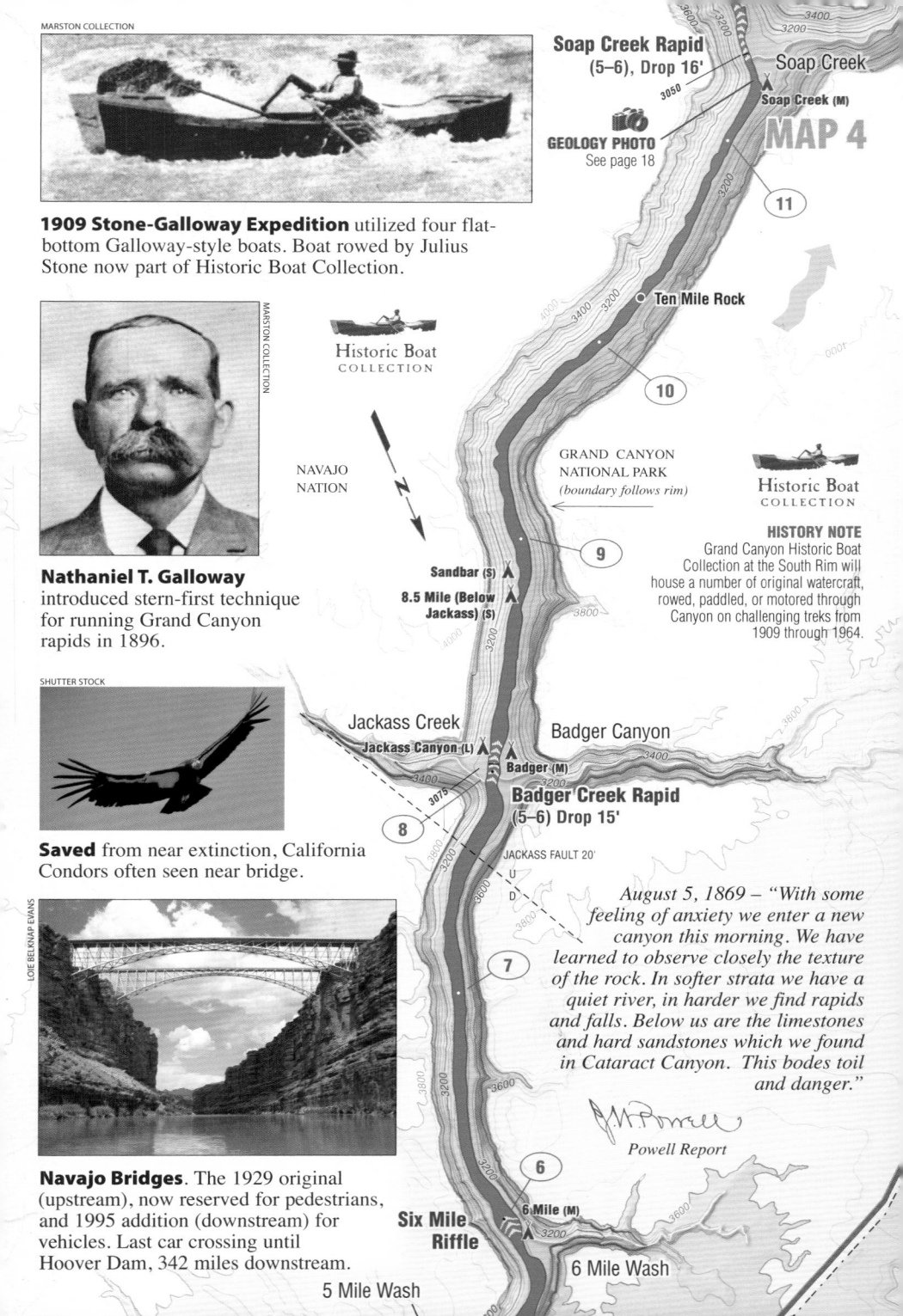

1909 Stone-Galloway Expedition utilized four flat-bottom Galloway-style boats. Boat rowed by Julius Stone now part of Historic Boat Collection.

Nathaniel T. Galloway introduced stern-first technique for running Grand Canyon rapids in 1896.

Saved from near extinction, California Condors often seen near bridge.

Navajo Bridges. The 1929 original (upstream), now reserved for pedestrians, and 1995 addition (downstream) for vehicles. Last car crossing until Hoover Dam, 342 miles downstream.

Soap Creek Rapid
(5–6), Drop 16'
3050
Soap Creek
Soap Creek (M)

MAP 4

GEOLOGY PHOTO
See page 18

11

Ten Mile Rock

10

Historic Boat
COLLECTION

NAVAJO
NATION

GRAND CANYON
NATIONAL PARK
(boundary follows rim)

Historic Boat
COLLECTION

HISTORY NOTE
Grand Canyon Historic Boat Collection at the South Rim will house a number of original watercraft, rowed, paddled, or motored through Canyon on challenging treks from 1909 through 1964.

Sandbar (S)
8.5 Mile (Below Jackass) (S)

9

Jackass Creek
Jackass Canyon (L)
Badger (M)
Badger Canyon
Badger Creek Rapid
(5–6) Drop 15'
3075

8

JACKASS FAULT 20'
U
D

7

August 5, 1869 – "With some feeling of anxiety we enter a new canyon this morning. We have learned to observe closely the texture of the rock. In softer strata we have a quiet river, in harder we find rapids and falls. Below us are the limestones and hard sandstones which we found in Cataract Canyon. This bodes toil and danger."

Powell Report

6

Six Mile Riffle
6 Mile (M)
3200

6 Mile Wash

5 Mile Wash

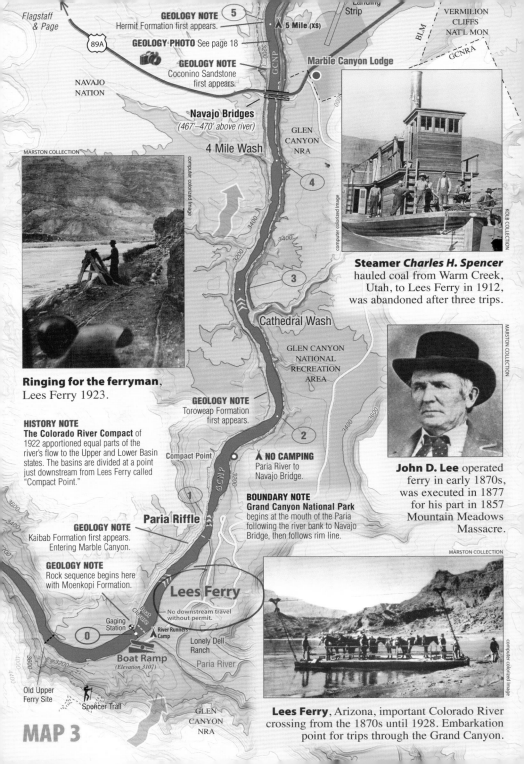

Flagstaff & Page

89A

NAVAJO NATION

GEOLOGY PHOTO See page 18

GEOLOGY NOTE 5
Hermit Formation first appears.

GEOLOGY NOTE
Coconino Sandstone
first appears.

5 Mile (XS)

Landing Strip

VERMILION CLIFFS NAT'L MON

BLM

GCNRA

Marble Canyon Lodge

GCNP

Navajo Bridges
(467'–470' above river)

GLEN CANYON NRA

4 Mile Wash

4

3200

3400

3400

3

MARSTON COLLECTION

computer colorized image

Ringing for the ferryman,
Lees Ferry 1923.

HISTORY NOTE
The Colorado River Compact of
1922 apportioned equal parts of the
river's flow to the Upper and Lower Basin
states. The basins are divided at a point
just downstream from Lees Ferry called
"Compact Point."

Cathedral Wash

GLEN CANYON NATIONAL RECREATION AREA

GEOLOGY NOTE
Toroweap Formation
first appears.

Compact Point

2

3000

3600

▲ **NO CAMPING**
Paria River to
Navajo Bridge.

GCNP

1

Paria Riffle

GEOLOGY NOTE
Kaibab Formation first appears.
Entering Marble Canyon.

GEOLOGY NOTE
Rock sequence begins here
with Moenkopi Formation.

3400

3600

3200

Lees Ferry

Boat Closure

Gaging Station

0

River Runners Camp

— No downstream travel
without permit.

Boat Ramp
(Elevation 3107)

Lonely Dell Ranch

Paria River

Old Upper Ferry Site

Spencer Trail

4000

3600

3200

GLEN CANYON NRA

MAP 3

BOUNDARY NOTE
Grand Canyon National Park
begins at the mouth of the Paria
following the river bank to Navajo
Bridge, then follows rim line.

KOLB COLLECTION

computer colorized image

Steamer *Charles H. Spencer*
hauled coal from Warm Creek,
Utah, to Lees Ferry in 1912,
was abandoned after three trips.

MARSTON COLLECTION

John D. Lee operated
ferry in early 1870s,
was executed in 1877
for his part in 1857
Mountain Meadows
Massacre.

MARSTON COLLECTION

computer colorized image

Lees Ferry, Arizona, important Colorado River
crossing from the 1870s until 1928. Embarkation
point for trips through the Grand Canyon.

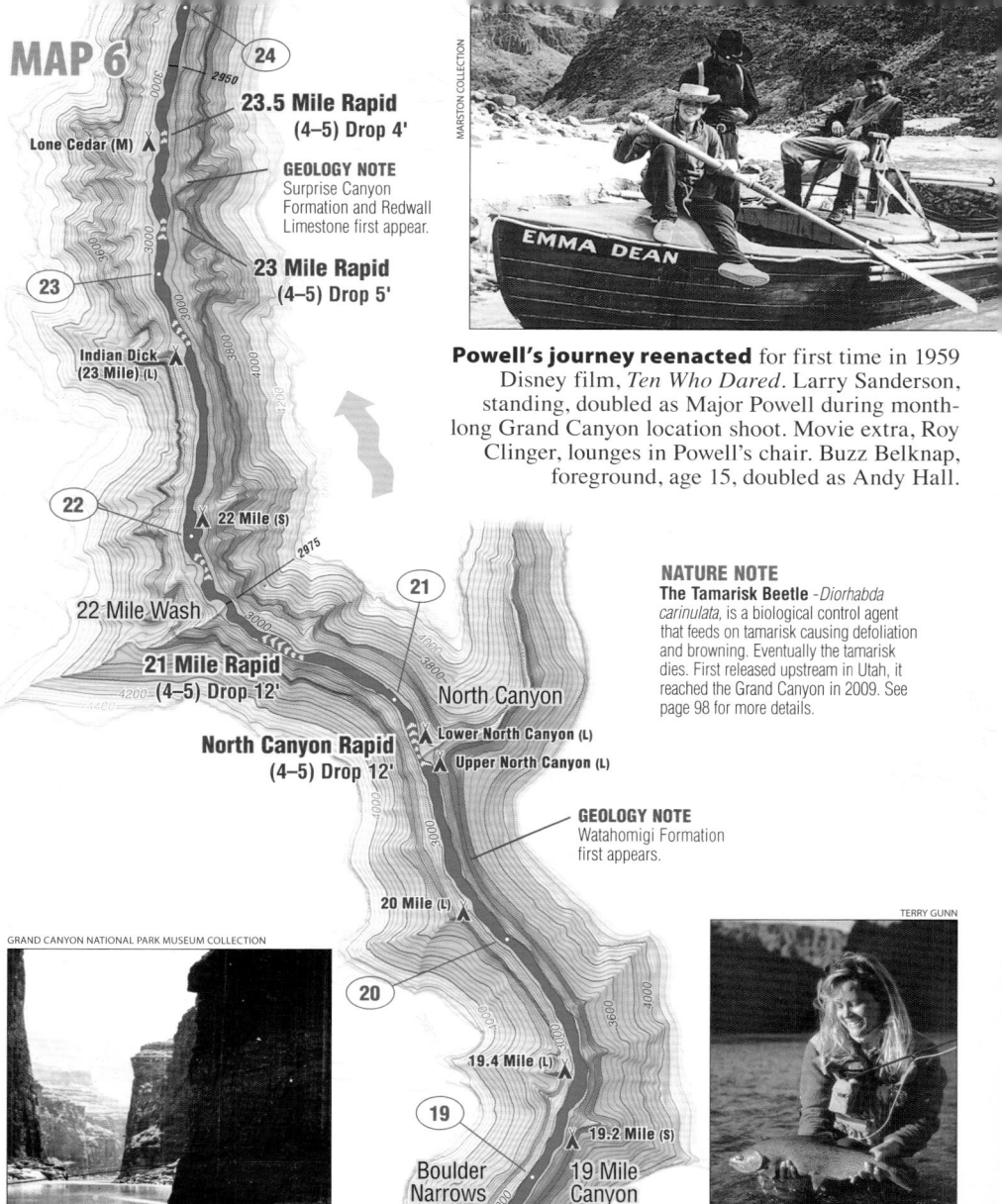

MAP 6

24

2950

23.5 Mile Rapid
(4–5) Drop 4'

Lone Cedar (M)

GEOLOGY NOTE
Surprise Canyon
Formation and Redwall
Limestone first appear.

23 Mile Rapid
(4–5) Drop 5'

23

Indian Dick
(23 Mile) (L)

MARSTON COLLECTION

Powell's journey reenacted for first time in 1959
Disney film, *Ten Who Dared*. Larry Sanderson,
standing, doubled as Major Powell during month-
long Grand Canyon location shoot. Movie extra, Roy
Clinger, lounges in Powell's chair. Buzz Belknap,
foreground, age 15, doubled as Andy Hall.

EMMA DEAN

22

22 Mile (S)

2975

22 Mile Wash

21

21 Mile Rapid
(4–5) Drop 12'

North Canyon

North Canyon Rapid
(4–5) Drop 12'

Lower North Canyon (L)

Upper North Canyon (L)

NATURE NOTE
The Tamarisk Beetle -*Diorhabda
carinulata*, is a biological control agent
that feeds on tamarisk causing defoliation
and browning. Eventually the tamarisk
dies. First released upstream in Utah, it
reached the Grand Canyon in 2009. See
page 98 for more details.

GEOLOGY NOTE
Watahomigi Formation
first appears.

20 Mile (L)

20

19.4 Mile (L)

19

19.2 Mile (S)

Boulder
Narrows

19 Mile
Canyon

GRAND CANYON NATIONAL PARK MUSEUM COLLECTION

TERRY GUNN

18 Mile
Ledges (M)

18 Mile
Wash

18 Mile
Wash (M)

GEOLOGY PHOTO
See page 19

GEOLOGY NOTE
Manakacha Formation
first appears.

18

Trout thrive in cold, clear
water downstream from
Glen Canyon Dam, home
to a top year-round U.S.
tailwater fishery.

"Noon day rest in Marble Canyon."
From John Wesley Powell's second
expedition. August 1872. Powell's
boat *Emma Dean* in background.

Redneck Rapid (3)

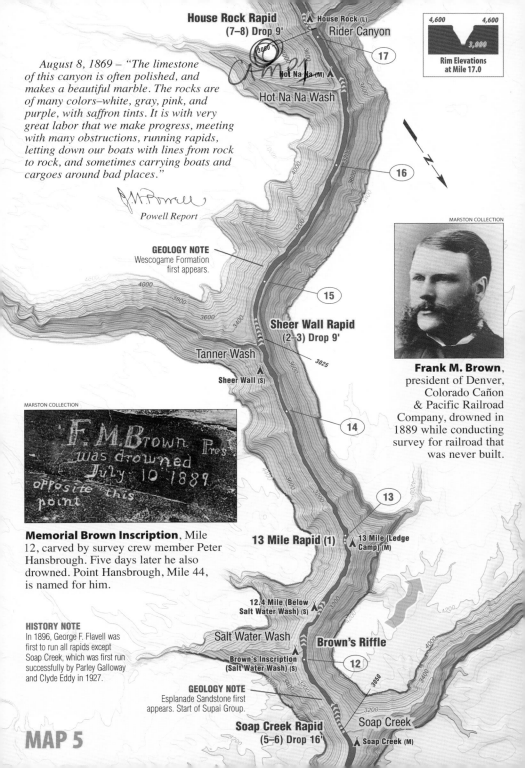

House Rock Rapid
(7–8) Drop 9'

House Rock (L)

Rider Canyon

4,600   4,600
3,000
**Rim Elevations
at Mile 17.0**

17

CAMP

3050

Hot Na Na (M)

Hot Na Na Wash

*August 8, 1869 – "The limestone
of this canyon is often polished, and
makes a beautiful marble. The rocks are
of many colors–white, gray, pink, and
purple, with saffron tints. It is with very
great labor that we make progress, meeting
with many obstructions, running rapids,
letting down our boats with lines from rock
to rock, and sometimes carrying boats and
cargoes around bad places."*

Powell Report

16

GEOLOGY NOTE
Wescogame Formation
first appears.

15

Sheer Wall Rapid
(2–3) Drop 9'

Tanner Wash

3025

Sheer Wall (S)

Frank M. Brown,
president of Denver,
Colorado Cañon
& Pacific Railroad
Company, drowned in
1889 while conducting
survey for railroad that
was never built.

14

'F.M.Brown Pres
was drowned
July 10 1889
opposite this
point

Memorial Brown Inscription, Mile
12, carved by survey crew member Peter
Hansbrough. Five days later he also
drowned. Point Hansbrough, Mile 44,
is named for him.

13

13 Mile (Ledge
Camp) (M)

13 Mile Rapid (1)

HISTORY NOTE
In 1896, George F. Flavell was
first to run all rapids except
Soap Creek, which was first run
successfully by Parley Galloway
and Clyde Eddy in 1927.

12.4 Mile (Below
Salt Water Wash) (S)

Salt Water Wash

Brown's Riffle

Brown's Inscription
(Salt Water Wash) (S)

12

3050

GEOLOGY NOTE
Esplanade Sandstone first
appears. Start of Supai Group.

Soap Creek Rapid
(5–6) Drop 16'

Soap Creek

Soap Creek (M)

MAP 5

MAP 8

MAP 8

Tatahatso Wash

37

4000
3600
3400
2850
4000

36 Mile Rapid
(4) Drop 4'

36

Bridge of Sighs

GEOLOGY NOTE
Muav Limestone first
appears. Beginning of
Tonto Group.

*August 9, 1869 – "The river turns
sharply to the east and seems inclosed
by a wall set with a million brilliant
gems. On coming nearer we find
fountains bursting from the rock high
overhead, and the spray in the sunshine
forms the gems which bedeck the wall.
The rocks are covered with mosses and
ferns and many beautiful flowering
plants. We name it Vasey's Paradise, in
honor of the botanist who traveled with
us last year."*

Powell Report

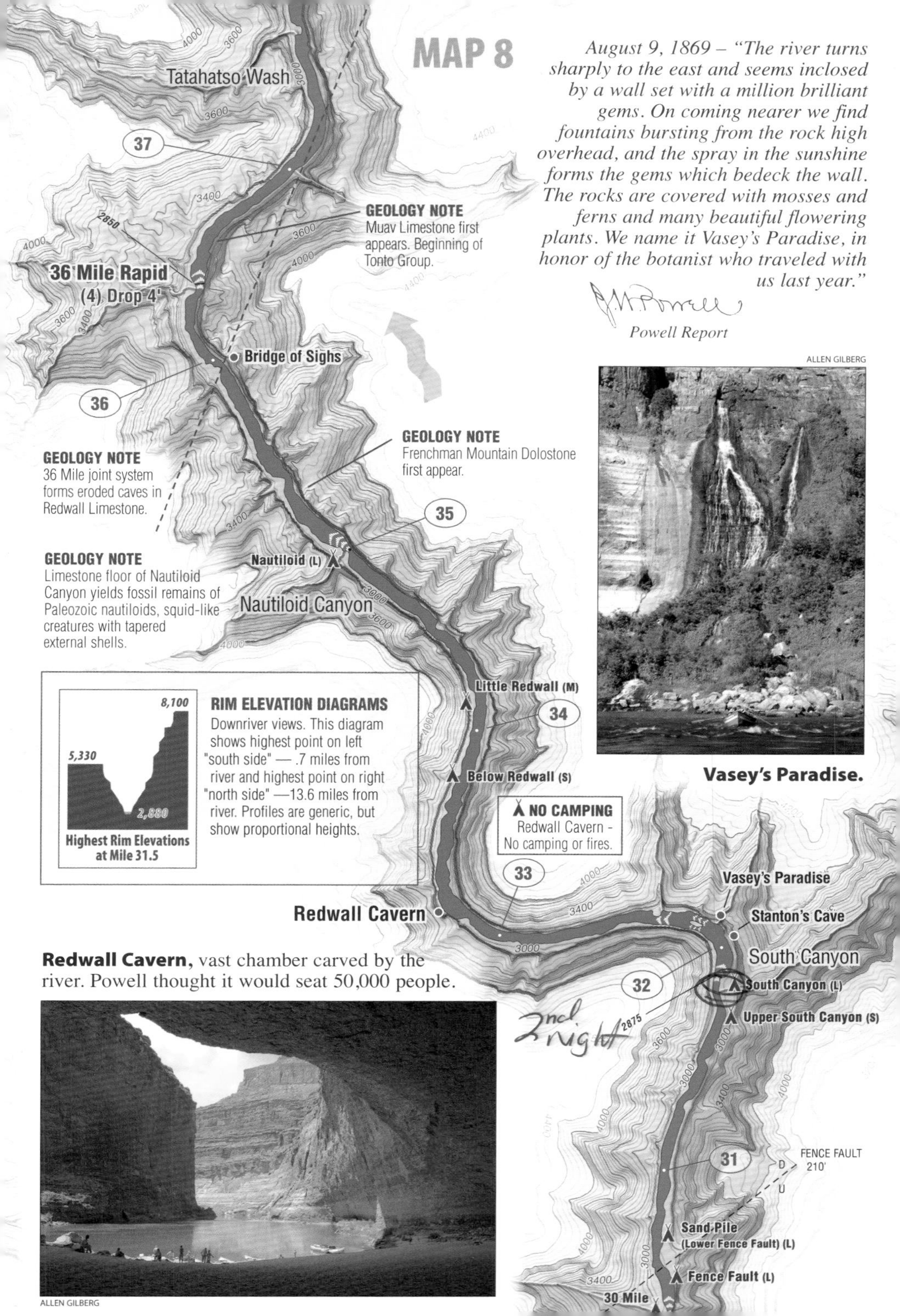

ALLEN GILBERG

GEOLOGY NOTE
36 Mile joint system
forms eroded caves in
Redwall Limestone.

GEOLOGY NOTE
Limestone floor of Nautiloid
Canyon yields fossil remains of
Paleozoic nautiloids, squid-like
creatures with tapered
external shells.

GEOLOGY NOTE
Frenchman Mountain Dolostone
first appear.

35

Nautiloid (L)

Nautiloid Canyon

Little Redwall (M)

34

Below Redwall (S)

RIM ELEVATION DIAGRAMS
Downriver views. This diagram
shows highest point on left
"south side" — .7 miles from
river and highest point on right
"north side" —13.6 miles from
river. Profiles are generic, but
show proportional heights.

8,100

5,330

2,880

**Highest Rim Elevations
at Mile 31.5**

✗ NO CAMPING
Redwall Cavern -
No camping or fires.

33

Vasey's Paradise.

Redwall Cavern

Redwall Cavern, vast chamber carved by the
river. Powell thought it would seat 50,000 people.

Vasey's Paradise

Stanton's Cave

South Canyon

32

South Canyon (L)

2nd night

2875

Upper South Canyon (S)

31

FENCE FAULT
210'

D

U

Sand Pile
(Lower Fence Fault) (L)

Fence Fault (L)

30 Mile

ALLEN GILBERG

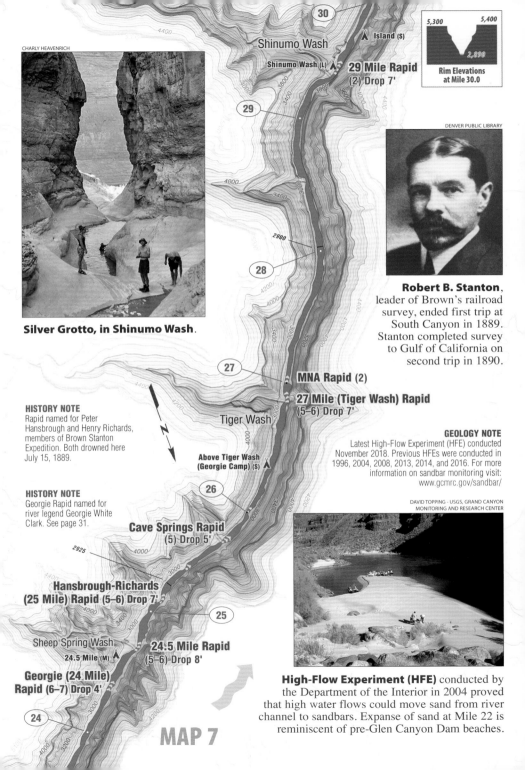

30

Shinumo Wash

↟ Island (s)

Shinumo Wash (L) ↟

29 Mile Rapid
(2) Drop 7'

29

**Rim Elevations
at Mile 30.0**

5,300   5,400

2,890

Silver Grotto, in Shinumo Wash.

28

Robert B. Stanton,
leader of Brown's railroad
survey, ended first trip at
South Canyon in 1889.
Stanton completed survey
to Gulf of California on
second trip in 1890.

27

MNA Rapid (2)

27 Mile (Tiger Wash) Rapid
(5–6) Drop 7'

Tiger Wash

HISTORY NOTE
Rapid named for Peter
Hansbrough and Henry Richards,
members of Brown Stanton
Expedition. Both drowned here
July 15, 1889.

**Above Tiger Wash
(Georgie Camp)** (S) ↟

GEOLOGY NOTE
Latest High-Flow Experiment (HFE) conducted
November 2018. Previous HFEs were conducted in
1996, 2004, 2008, 2013, 2014, and 2016. For more
information on sandbar monitoring visit:
www.gcmrc.gov/sandbar/

26

HISTORY NOTE
Georgie Rapid named for
river legend Georgie White
Clark. See page 31.

Cave Springs Rapid
(5) Drop 5'

2925

**Hansbrough-Richards
(25 Mile) Rapid** (5–6) Drop 7'

25

Sheep Spring Wash

24.5 Mile Rapid
(5–6) Drop 8'

24.5 Mile (M) ↟

**Georgie (24 Mile)
Rapid** (6–7) Drop 4'

24

MAP 7

High-Flow Experiment (HFE) conducted by
the Department of the Interior in 2004 proved
that high water flows could move sand from river
channel to sandbars. Expanse of sand at Mile 22 is
reminiscent of pre-Glen Canyon Dam beaches.

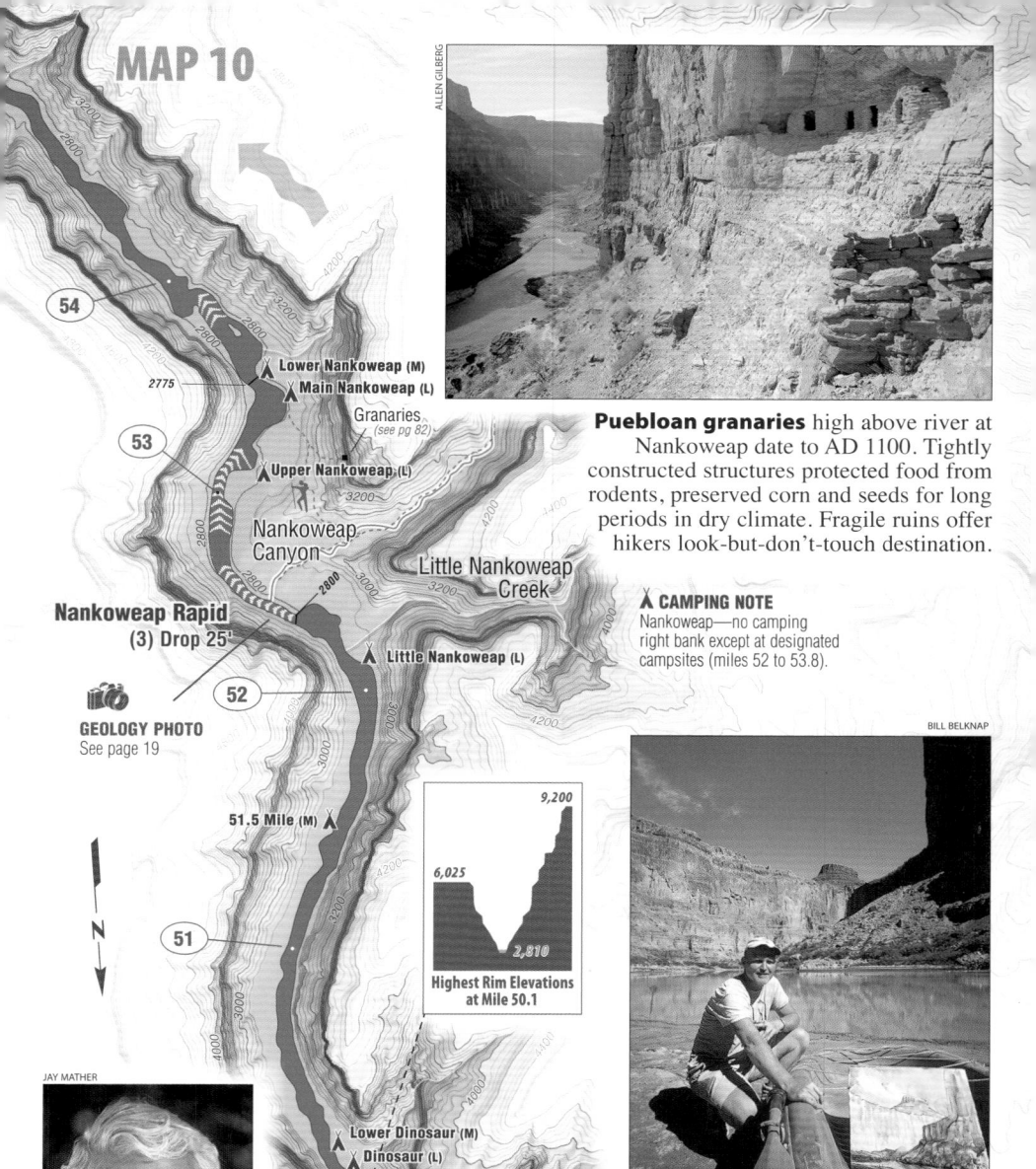

MAP 10

ALLEN GILBERG

54

Lower Nankoweap (M)
Main Nankoweap (L)

2775

53

Granaries
(see pg 82)

Upper Nankoweap (L)

Nankoweap
Canyon

Little Nankoweap
Creek

Puebloan granaries high above river at Nankoweap date to AD 1100. Tightly constructed structures protected food from rodents, preserved corn and seeds for long periods in dry climate. Fragile ruins offer hikers look-but-don't-touch destination.

Nankoweap Rapid
(3) Drop 25'

Little Nankoweap (L)

GEOLOGY PHOTO
See page 19

52

⋏ **CAMPING NOTE**
Nankoweap—no camping right bank except at designated campsites (miles 52 to 53.8).

BILL BELKNAP

51.5 Mile (M)

9,200

6,025

51

2,810

Highest Rim Elevations at Mile 50.1

JAY MATHER

Lower Dinosaur (M)
Dinosaur (L)

50

Nevada artist Cliff Segerblom posing with watercolor of upstream view from Nankoweap on low-water Sportyak trip in 1963. Segerblom developed artist workshops on commercial trips. Many outfitters now offer specialty trips featuring history, archaeology, geology, art.

In late 1960s Sierra Club's David Brower led successful fight to defeat dams in Grand Canyon.

U D

49

EMINENCE BREAK
FAULT, 100'

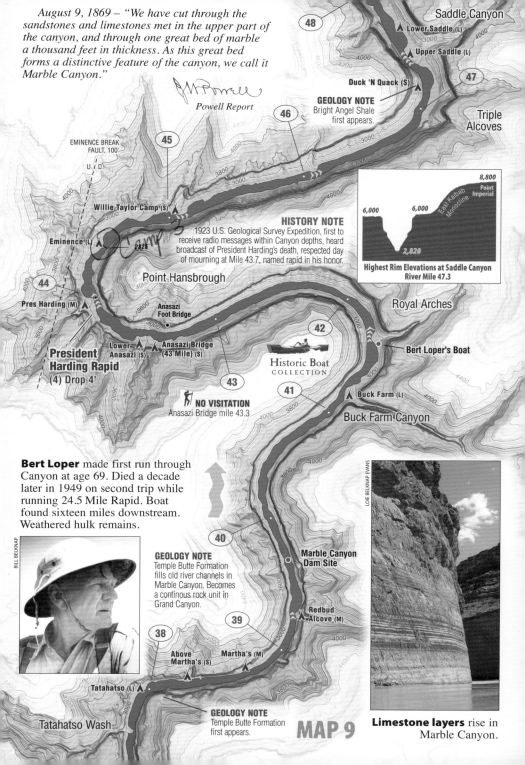

August 9, 1869 – "We have cut through the sandstones and limestones met in the upper part of the canyon, and through one great bed of marble a thousand feet in thickness. As this great bed forms a distinctive feature of the canyon, we call it Marble Canyon."

Powell Report

48

Saddle Canyon

Lower Saddle (L)
Upper Saddle (L)

Duck 'N Quack (S)

47

Triple Alcoves

GEOLOGY NOTE
Bright Angel Shale first appears.

46

45

EMINENCE BREAK FAULT, 100'
U / D

Willie Taylor Camp (S)

Eminence (L)

HISTORY NOTE
1923 U.S. Geological Survey Expedition, first to receive radio messages within Canyon depths, heard broadcast of President Harding's death, respected day of mourning at Mile 43.7, named rapid in his honor.

8,800
6,000   6,000   Point Imperial
East Kaibab Monocline
2,820

Highest Rim Elevations at Saddle Canyon River Mile 47.3

Point Hansbrough

44

Pres Harding (M)

Anasazi Foot Bridge

42

Royal Arches

Bert Loper's Boat

Historic Boat COLLECTION

President Harding Rapid (4) Drop 4'

Lower Anasazi (S)   Anasazi Bridge (43 Mile) (S)

43

41

Buck Farm (L)

Buck Farm Canyon

NO VISITATION
Anasazi Bridge mile 43.3

Bert Loper made first run through Canyon at age 69. Died a decade later in 1949 on second trip while running 24.5 Mile Rapid. Boat found sixteen miles downstream. Weathered hulk remains.

40

Marble Canyon Dam Site

GEOLOGY NOTE
Temple Butte Formation fills old river channels in Marble Canyon. Becomes a continous rock unit in Grand Canyon.

Redbud Alcove (M)

38

39

Above Martha's (S)   Martha's (M)

Tatahatso (L)

Tatahatso Wash

GEOLOGY NOTE
Temple Butte Formation first appears.

MAP 9

LOIE BELKNAP EVANS

BILL BELKNAP

Limestone layers rise in Marble Canyon.

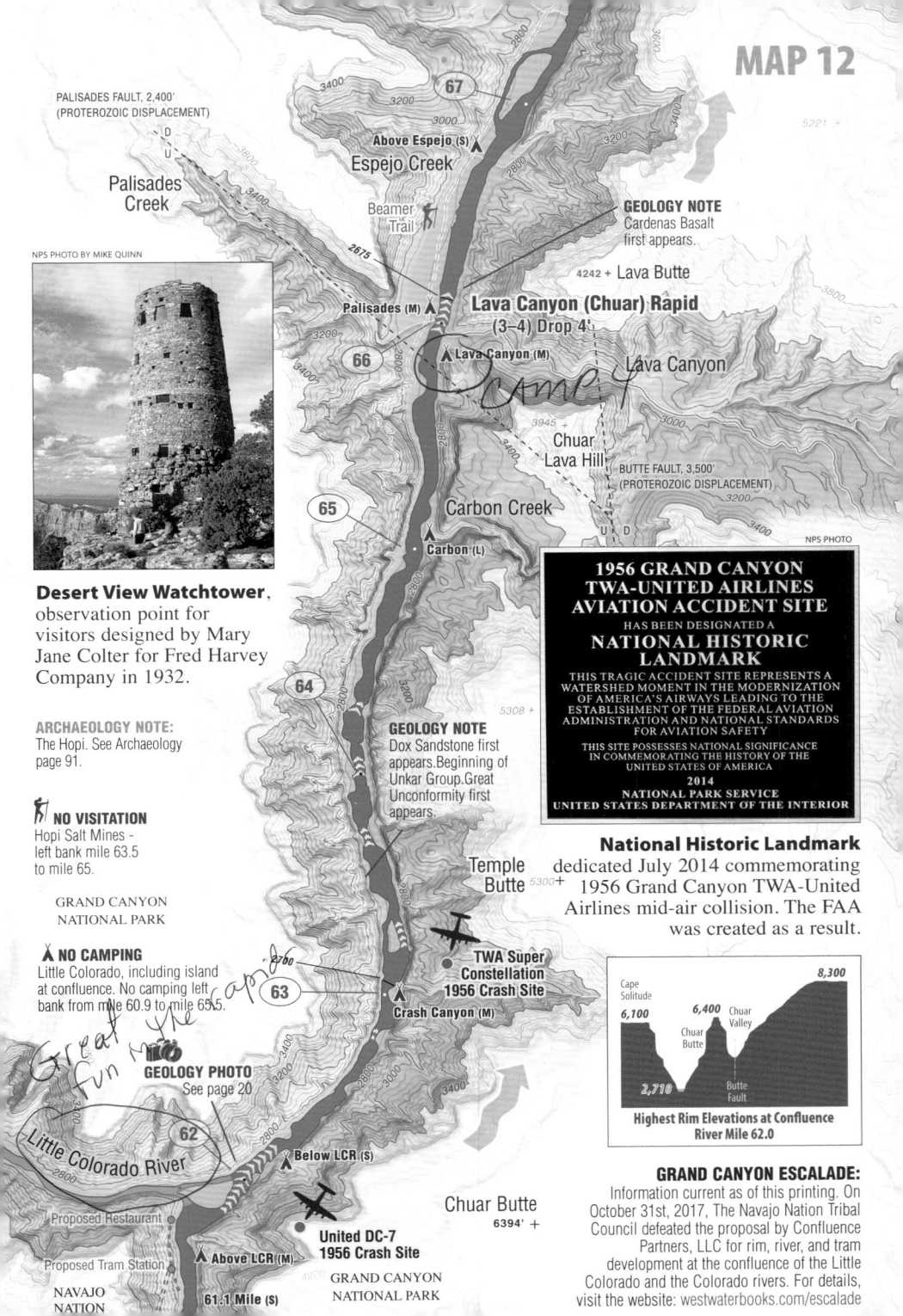

MAP 12

PALISADES FAULT, 2,400'
(PROTEROZOIC DISPLACEMENT)

Palisades
Creek

67

Above Espejo (S)
Espejo Creek

3400
3000
2800
3200
3600
3800
5221

Beamer
Trail

2675

GEOLOGY NOTE
Cardenas Basalt
first appears.

4242 + Lava Butte

Palisades (M)

66

Lava Canyon (Chuar) Rapid
(3–4) Drop 4'

Lava Canyon (M)   Lava Canyon

3945 +
Chuar
Lava Hill

BUTTE FAULT, 3,500'
(PROTEROZOIC DISPLACEMENT)

NPS PHOTO BY MIKE QUINN

65

Carbon Creek

Carbon (L)

NPS PHOTO

Desert View Watchtower,
observation point for
visitors designed by Mary
Jane Colter for Fred Harvey
Company in 1932.

64

ARCHAEOLOGY NOTE:
The Hopi. See Archaeology
page 91.

5308 +

GEOLOGY NOTE
Dox Sandstone first
appears. Beginning of
Unkar Group. Great
Unconformity first
appears.

**1956 GRAND CANYON
TWA-UNITED AIRLINES
AVIATION ACCIDENT SITE**
HAS BEEN DESIGNATED A
**NATIONAL HISTORIC
LANDMARK**
THIS TRAGIC ACCIDENT SITE REPRESENTS A
WATERSHED MOMENT IN THE MODERNIZATION
OF AMERICA'S AIRWAYS LEADING TO THE
ESTABLISHMENT OF THE FEDERAL AVIATION
ADMINISTRATION AND NATIONAL STANDARDS
FOR AVIATION SAFETY

THIS SITE POSSESSES NATIONAL SIGNIFICANCE
IN COMMEMORATING THE HISTORY OF THE
UNITED STATES OF AMERICA
2014
NATIONAL PARK SERVICE
UNITED STATES DEPARTMENT OF THE INTERIOR

NO VISITATION
Hopi Salt Mines -
left bank mile 63.5
to mile 65.

GRAND CANYON
NATIONAL PARK

NO CAMPING
Little Colorado, including island
at confluence. No camping left
bank from mile 60.9 to mile 65.5.

Temple
Butte 5300+

National Historic Landmark
dedicated July 2014 commemorating
1956 Grand Canyon TWA-United
Airlines mid-air collision. The FAA
was created as a result.

2760

63

**TWA Super
Constellation
1956 Crash Site**

Crash Canyon (M)

Cape
Solitude
6,100

6,400
Chuar
Valley

8,300

Chuar
Butte

GEOLOGY PHOTO
See page 20

2,710

Butte
Fault

**Highest Rim Elevations at Confluence
River Mile 62.0**

Little Colorado River

62

2800

Below LCR (S)

Chuar Butte
6394' +

Proposed Restaurant

GRAND CANYON ESCALADE:
Information current as of this printing. On
October 31st, 2017, The Navajo Nation Tribal
Council defeated the proposal by Confluence
Partners, LLC for rim, river, and tram
development at the confluence of the Little
Colorado and the Colorado rivers. For details,
see the website: westwaterbooks.com/escalade

Proposed Tram Station

**United DC-7
1956 Crash Site**

Above LCR (M)

GRAND CANYON
NATIONAL PARK

NAVAJO
NATION   61.1 Mile (S)

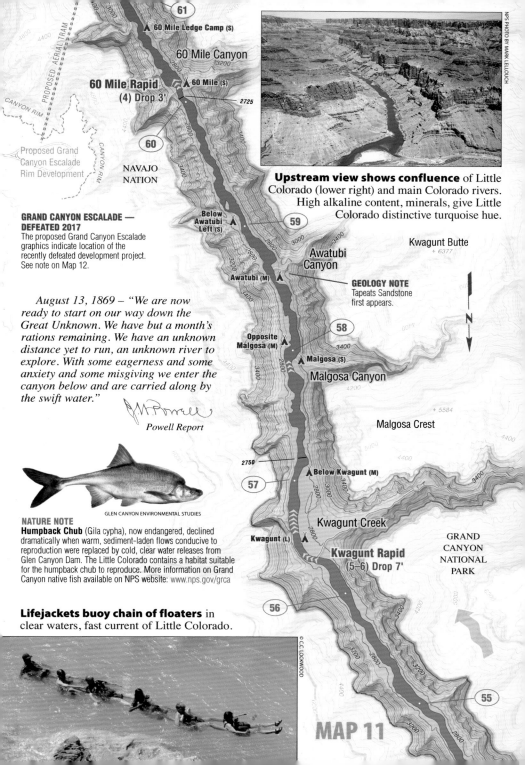

61

60 Mile Ledge Camp (S)

60 Mile Canyon
3200

60 Mile Rapid
(4) Drop 3'

60 Mile (S)

2725

60

PROPOSED AERIAL TRAM

CANYON RIM

Proposed Grand
Canyon Escalade
Rim Development

CANYON RIM

NAVAJO
NATION

Upstream view shows confluence of Little
Colorado (lower right) and main Colorado rivers.
High alkaline content, minerals, give Little
Colorado distinctive turquoise hue.

NPS PHOTO BY MARK LELLOUCH

GRAND CANYON ESCALADE —
DEFEATED 2017
The proposed Grand Canyon Escalade
graphics indicate location of the
recently defeated development project.
See note on Map 12.

Below
Awatubi
Left (S)

59

Awatubi
Canyon

Kwagunt Butte
+ 6377

Awatubi (M)

GEOLOGY NOTE
Tapeats Sandstone
first appears.

N

August 13, 1869 – "We are now
ready to start on our way down the
Great Unknown. We have but a month's
rations remaining. We have an unknown
distance yet to run, an unknown river to
explore. With some eagerness and some
anxiety and some misgiving we enter the
canyon below and are carried along by
the swift water."

Opposite
Malgosa (M)

58

Malgosa (S)

Malgosa Canyon

Powell Report

+ 5584

Malgosa Crest

2750

Below Kwagunt (M)

57

NATURE NOTE
Humpback Chub (Gila cypha), now endangered, declined
dramatically when warm, sediment-laden flows conducive to
reproduction were replaced by cold, clear water releases from
Glen Canyon Dam. The Little Colorado contains a habitat suitable
for the humpback chub to reproduce. More information on Grand
Canyon native fish available on NPS website: www.nps.gov/grca

GLEN CANYON ENVIRONMENTAL STUDIES

Kwagunt Creek

Kwagunt (L)

Kwagunt Rapid
(5–6) Drop 7'

GRAND
CANYON
NATIONAL
PARK

56

Lifejackets buoy chain of floaters in
clear waters, fast current of Little Colorado.

© C.C. LOCKWOOD

55

MAP 11

MAP 14

Hance Rapid drops **30 feet** in half-mile at start of Granite Gorge. Massive basalt dike marks entrance.

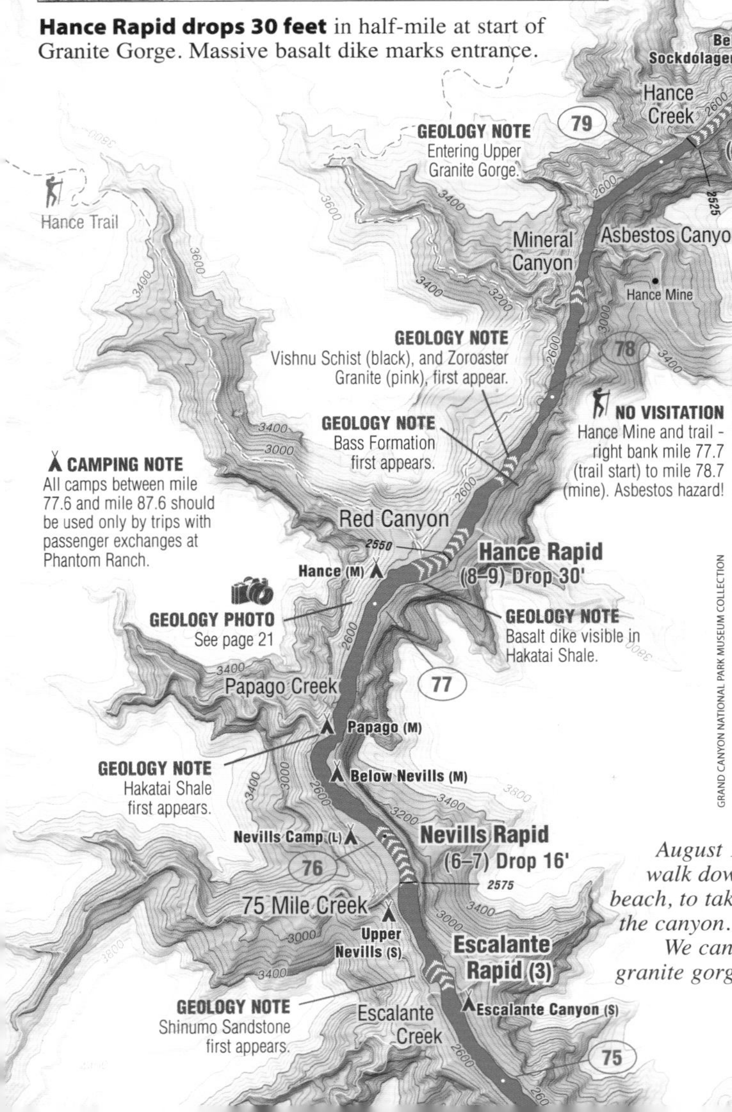

Grandview Trail

Cottonwood Creek

81

GEOLOGY NOTE
By this point, all formations in the Grand Canyon rock sequence have appeared except lava flows downstream at Mile 179.

Tonto Trail

80

Below Sockdolager (S)

Hance Creek

79

Sockdolager Rapid
(7–9) Drop 19'

GEOLOGY NOTE
Entering Upper Granite Gorge.

Hance Trail

Mineral Canyon

Asbestos Canyon

Hance Mine

"Captain" John Hance, miner, rancher, guide, storyteller, was South Rim's first white settler. On porch with two Abert's squirrels, June 1899.

GEOLOGY NOTE
Vishnu Schist (black), and Zoroaster Granite (pink), first appear.

78

NO VISITATION
Hance Mine and trail - right bank mile 77.7 (trail start) to mile 78.7 (mine). Asbestos hazard!

GEOLOGY NOTE
Bass Formation first appears.

CAMPING NOTE
All camps between mile 77.6 and mile 87.6 should be used only by trips with passenger exchanges at Phantom Ranch.

Red Canyon

Hance (M)

Hance Rapid
(8–9) Drop 30'

GEOLOGY NOTE
Basalt dike visible in Hakatai Shale.

GEOLOGY PHOTO
See page 21

Papago Creek

77

Papago (M)

Below Nevills (M)

GEOLOGY NOTE
Hakatai Shale first appears.

Nevills Camp (L)

Nevills Rapid
(6–7) Drop 16'

GRAND CANYON NATIONAL PARK MUSEUM COLLECTION

76

75 Mile Creek

Upper Nevills (S)

Escalante Rapid (3)

August 14, 1869 – "At daybreak we walk down the bank on a little sandy beach, to take a view of a new feature in the canyon. The river enters the gneiss! We can see but a little way into the granite gorge, but it looks threatening."

GEOLOGY NOTE
Shinumo Sandstone first appears.

Escalante Creek

Escalante Canyon (S)

75

Powell Report

ALLEN GILBERG

Nevills was first to offer commercial river trips through Canyon, developed wooden Cataract boat called a sadiron.

Historic Boat
COLLECTION

Norman D. Nevills at the oars of the *Wen*, used on seven Canyon runs between 1938-1949.

Wide spot in Canyon, looking upstream toward Unkar Rapid and Delta, was site of Cohonina and Puebloan habitation AD 950-1150. Park Service path leads to terrace above river where trails wind among dwelling sites excavated in 1967-68. Largest known prehistoric settlement along the river.

7,300   8,000

2,600

Highest Rim Elevations at Mile 73.8

Upper Rattlesnake (L)   3400

Below Granary Left (xS)   2600   3200

74   3000

Unkar Creek

Unkar Delta
(See Archaeology page 89)   2800

Upper Unkar (M)

Unkar Left (L)

Unkar Rapid
(6–7) Drop 25'   73

Cardenas Creek   72

Cardenas (M)   2800

🏹 **NO VISITATION**
Furnace Flats - right bank
mile 71.5 to mile 72.2.

Furnace Flats

2625   71

4761 +

BASALT CANYON FAULT, 430'
(PROTEROZOIC DISPLACEMENT)

U
D

Tanner Trail   + 4281

3000   2800

3200

3400

Lower
Basalt (M)

Basalt Rapid (2)   70

Basalt Canyon   3200

Below Tanner
Rapid (M)

Tanner Rapid
(4) Drop 20'

GEOLOGY NOTE
Nankoweap Formation first
appears above black lava.

Tanner Canyon   2650   69

D
U

Tanner (L)

Upper Tanner (68 Mile) (L)   BUTTE FAULT
1,100'
(PROTEROZOIC
DISPLACEMENT)

Beamer Trail   68

Comanche (S)

Comanche Creek   3000

Espejo Creek   2600

3200
3400   67

MAP 13

MAP 16

Salt Creek (S) ▲

Salt Creek Rapid
((3) Drop 5'

Salt Creek

(93)

Trinity Creek

Above Salt Creek (M) ▲

GRAND CANYON NATIONAL PARK MUSEUM COLLECTION

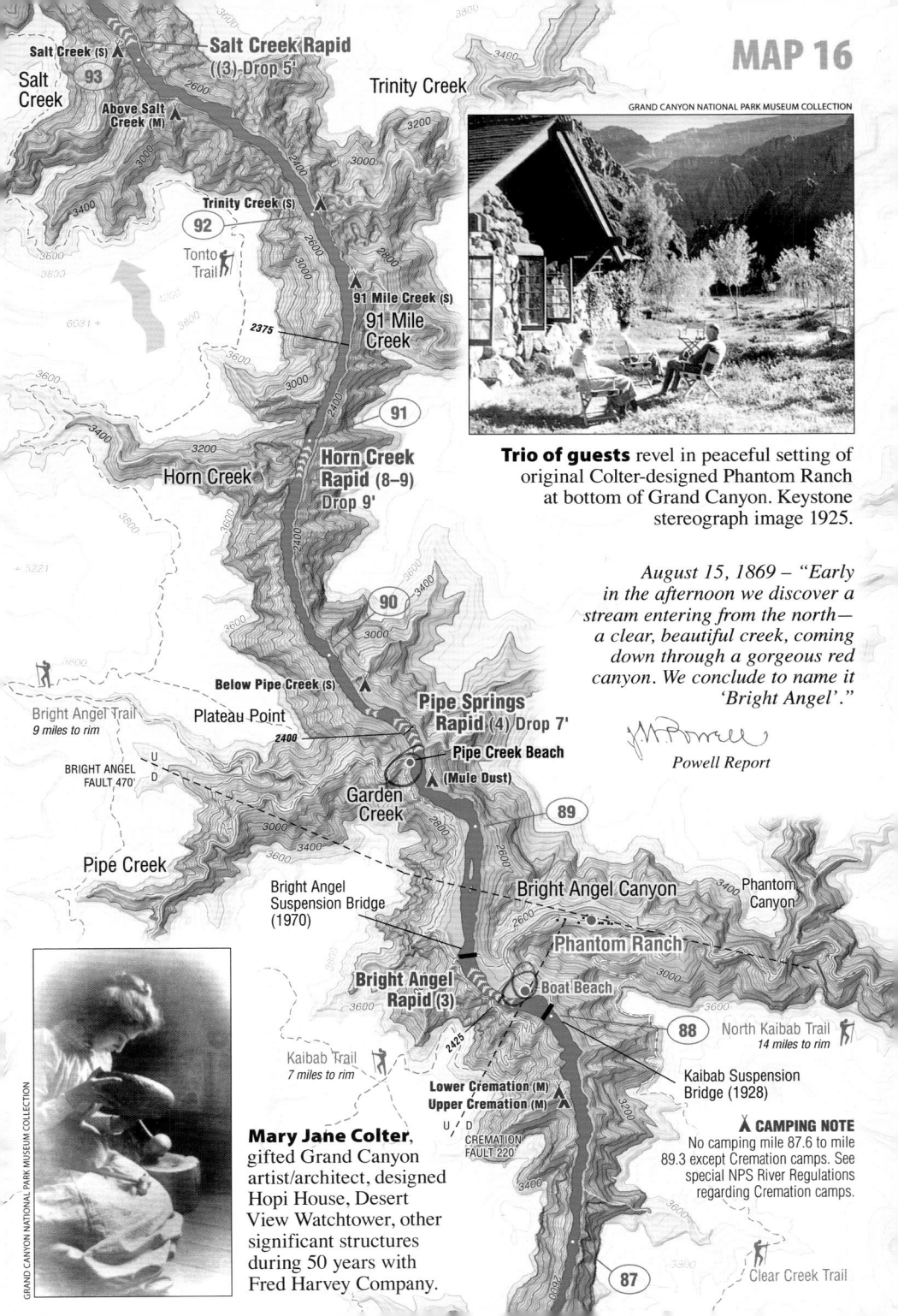

Trinity Creek (S) ▲

(92)

Tonto Trail ⚡

91 Mile Creek (S) ▲

2375

91 Mile Creek

(91)

Horn Creek Rapid (8–9) Drop 9'

Horn Creek

(90)

Trio of guests revel in peaceful setting of original Colter-designed Phantom Ranch at bottom of Grand Canyon. Keystone stereograph image 1925.

August 15, 1869 – "Early in the afternoon we discover a stream entering from the north— a clear, beautiful creek, coming down through a gorgeous red canyon. We conclude to name it 'Bright Angel'."

J.W. Powell

Powell Report

Below Pipe Creek (S) ▲

Bright Angel Trail
9 miles to rim

Plateau Point

Pipe Springs Rapid (4) Drop 7'

2400

Pipe Creek Beach

BRIGHT ANGEL FAULT 470'

(Mule Dust) ▲

Garden Creek

(89)

Pipe Creek

Bright Angel Suspension Bridge (1970)

Bright Angel Canyon

Phantom Canyon

Phantom Ranch

Bright Angel Rapid (3)

Boat Beach

Kaibab Trail
7 miles to rim

(88) North Kaibab Trail
14 miles to rim

2425

Lower Cremation (M)
Upper Cremation (M) ▲

Kaibab Suspension Bridge (1928)

CREMATION FAULT 220'

⚤ **CAMPING NOTE**
No camping mile 87.6 to mile 89.3 except Cremation camps. See special NPS River Regulations regarding Cremation camps.

Mary Jane Colter, gifted Grand Canyon artist/architect, designed Hopi House, Desert View Watchtower, other significant structures during 50 years with Fred Harvey Company.

GRAND CANYON NATIONAL PARK MUSEUM COLLECTION

(87)

Clear Creek Trail

'Rastus,' the mule, packed washing machine down Bright Angel Trail to Phantom Ranch in 1939. Sure-footed mules still pack loads in and out today.

Cremation Creek

Tonto Trail

86

85 Mile Rapid **(3–5)**

August 14, 1869 – "The gorge is black and narrow below, red and gray and flaring above, with crags and angular projections on the walls. Down in these grand gloomy depths we glide, ever listening, ever watching."

Powell Report

Zoroaster Rapid (5–7) Drop 5'

2450

85'

Camp 15

Zoroaster (M)

Zoroaster Canyon

▲ **Below Clear Creek (S)**

Clear Creek

▲ **Clear Creek (S)**

Lonetree Canyon

MAILED BY MULE AT THE BOTTOM OF THE GRAND CANYON PHANTOM RANCH

84

83 Mile Rapid (3–6) Drop 7'

7,200   8,060

GEOLOGY NOTE
Canyon geologist Clarence E. Dutton gave names from Asian religions to some topographic formations.

2,435

Highest Rim Elevations at Mile 86.3

☓ CAMPING NOTE
All camps between mile 77.6 and mile 87.6 should be used only by trips with passenger exchanges at Phantom Ranch.

Boulder Creek

83

GEOLOGY PHOTO
See page 21

2475

Grapevine Rapid (6–8) Drop 17'

Grapevine Creek

Grapevine (L) ☓

82

JUSTIN HOWE

Vishnu Creek

Cottonwood Creek

Tonto Trail

81

Boat Beach at Phantom Ranch with mules on bridge in background. Trail to historic ranch follows Bright Angel Creek. Small store sells sundries, has post office. Frequent departure, arrival point for river passengers.

MAP 15

MAP 18

CLINE LIBRARY - P. T. REILLY COLLECTION

Math Professor Dr. Harvey Butchart hiked more than 12,000 miles in the Canyon, investigated most of its trails.

Tonto Trail

106

2225

Ruby Rapid
(5–6) Drop 11'

Ruby Canyon

105

104 Mile Rapid
(5) Drop 4'
Emerald (M)

104

103 Mile (M)

New Shady Grove (M)

NPS PHOTO - MIKE QUINN

Turquoise Rapid
(3–5) Drop 4'

Turquoise Canyon

103

2250

102

Sapphire Rapid
(6) Drop 8'

Sapphire Canyon

Tonto Trail

Agate Rapid (3)

Agate Canyon

101

"Clouds are playing in the canyon today. Sometimes they roll down in great masses, filling the gorge with gloom; sometimes they hang aloft from wall to wall and cover the canyon with a roof of impending storm…"

Powell Report

Nixon Rock

Nixon Rock (4)

2275

Lower Tuna (Willie's Necktie) Rapid (4) Drop 10'

Lower Tuna (L)

100

Tuna Creek Rapid
(5–7) Drop 10'

Tuna Creek

Above Tuna Rapids (XS)

ROBERT B. STANTON

computer colorized image

Placid-looking Crystal Rapid in 1890.

99

Crystal Rapid
(10) Drop 17'

Slate Creek

∧ Ego Beach (S)

∧ Crystal (M)

Crystal Creek

Tonto Trail

98

DID ½

6,700   8,000

2,315

Highest Rim Elevations at Mile 98.7

GEOLOGY NOTE
Crystal Rapid, see
Geology page 10

HISTORY NOTE
In 1983 National Park Service
asked passengers to walk around
Crystal Rapid, dangerously
swollen by unprecendented
summer runoffs in the West.

Boucher (M) ∧

Boucher Rapid
(4–5) Drop 13'

Boucher Creek

2325

97

© 2007 – RUDI PETSCHEK

Boucher Trail

Schist (M) ∧

96

Travertine Canyon

fun

Hermit Rapid
(8–9) Drop 15'

Hermit (M) ∧

Hermit Creek

Debris flow in 1966 tumbled boulders from
Crystal Creek, choking Colorado. Overnight Crystal
became major rapid. Connie Tibbitts navigating a
muddy Crystal Rapid early 1980s.

95

94 Mile Creek

∧ 94 Mile Canyon (XS)

2350

fun (big water due to flow)

*August 17, 1869 – "It is especially
cold in the rain tonight. The little canvas
we have is rotten and useless; the rubber
ponchos have all been lost; we have not a
blanket apiece. So we build a fire; but the
rain, coming down in torrents, extinguishes
it, and we sit up all night on the rocks,
shivering, and are more exhausted by the
night's discomfort than by the day's toil."*

Monument
Creek

Granite Rapid
(8–9) Drop 18'

Granite (L) ∧

Camp 94

Salt Creek Rapid
(3) Drop 5'

93

Salt Creek (S) ∧

Above Salt Creek (M)

MAP 17

Powell Report

Tonto Trail

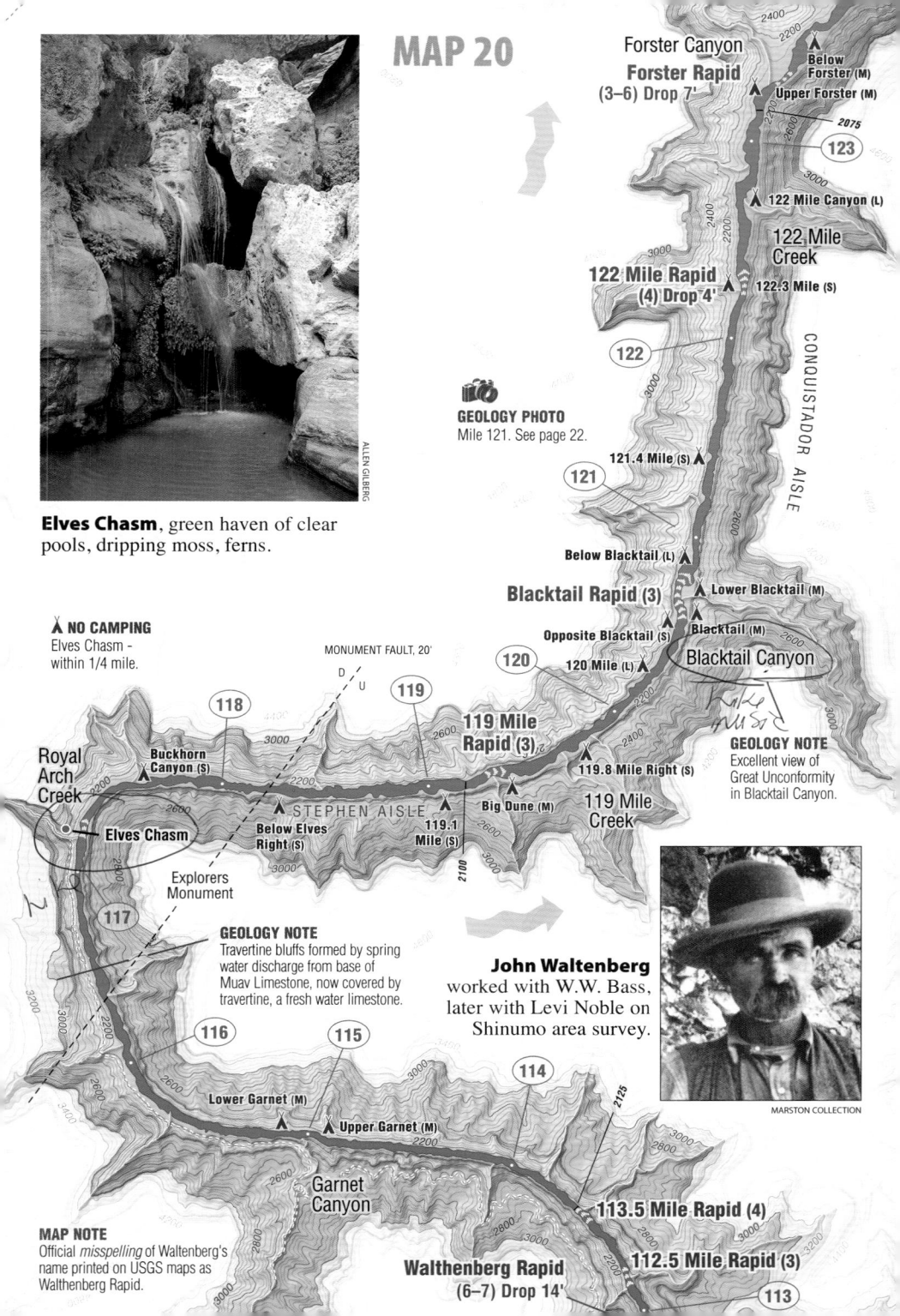

MAP 20

Elves Chasm, green haven of clear pools, dripping moss, ferns.

ALLEN GILBERG

GEOLOGY PHOTO
Mile 121. See page 22.

Forster Canyon
Forster Rapid
(3–6) Drop 7'

Below Forster (M)
Upper Forster (M)

2075

123

122 Mile Canyon (L)

122 Mile Creek

122 Mile Rapid
(4) Drop 4'

122.3 Mile (S)

122

121.4 Mile (S)

121

Below Blacktail (L)

Blacktail Rapid (3)

Lower Blacktail (M)

Opposite Blacktail (S)

Blacktail (M)

Blacktail Canyon

120 Mile (L)

120

CONQUISTADOR AISLE

GEOLOGY NOTE
Excellent view of Great Unconformity in Blacktail Canyon.

☓ NO CAMPING
Elves Chasm – within 1/4 mile.

MONUMENT FAULT, 20'
D U

118

119

119 Mile Rapid (3)

119.8 Mile Right (S)

119 Mile Creek

Royal Arch Creek

Buckhorn Canyon (S)

STEPHEN AISLE

Below Elves Right (S)

Big Dune (M)

119.1 Mile (S)

Elves Chasm

Explorers Monument

117

GEOLOGY NOTE
Travertine bluffs formed by spring water discharge from base of Muav Limestone, now covered by travertine, a fresh water limestone.

John Waltenberg
worked with W.W. Bass, later with Levi Noble on Shinumo area survey.

MARSTON COLLECTION

116

115

114

Lower Garnet (M)

Upper Garnet (M)

2125

Garnet Canyon

113.5 Mile Rapid (4)

112.5 Mile Rapid (3)

113

MAP NOTE
Official *misspelling* of Waltenberg's name printed on USGS maps as Walthenberg Rapid.

Walthenberg Rapid
(6–7) Drop 14'

Horse hangs after kicking out of Bass Cable cage, 1917.

6,625 **7,500**

2,165

Highest Rim Elevations at Mile 111

N

Historic Boat
COLLECTION

HISTORY NOTE
The *Ross Wheeler*, steel boat abandoned by motion picture man Charles S. Russell in 1915, remains at foot of South Bass Trail. Designed and built by Bert Loper; named for a local steamboat pilot—Roswell "Ross" Wheeler.

Waltenberg (S)

Waltenberg Canyon

112

Tonto Trail

2150

Hakatai Rapid
(3–4) Drop 8'

Hakatai Canyon

111

Copper Canyon

NO VISITATION
Bass Mine, Hakatai Canyon - right bank mile 111.5. Asbestos hazard!

110 Mile Rapid
(2–3) Drop 17'

2175

Camp

110

110 Mile (L)

Burro Canyon

South Bass Trail

GEOLOGY PHOTO
Mile 109. See page 22.

NO CAMPING
Shinumo Creek - within 100 yards.

WHEELER FOLD
500'

Shinumo Rapid
(3–4) Drop 8'

109

Shinumo Creek

Bass (L)

Bass Canyon

Ross Wheeler (S)

Bass Crossing (xs)

Parkins Inscription (S)

Beautiful
Waterfall

Tonto Trail

Hotauta (M)

Hotauta Canyon

Bass Rapid
(4–5) Drop 5'

North Bass Trail

Serpentine Canyon

108

Serpentine Rapid
(6–7) Drop 12'

107

106

2225

August 19, 1869 – "In running a rapid the pioneer boat is upset by a wave. The river is rough and swift and we are unable to land, but cling to the boat and are carried down over another rapid. The men in the boats above see our trouble, but they are caught in whirlpools and are spinning about in eddies, and it seems a long time before they come to our relief."

Powell Report

MAP 19

William W. Bass, with Joe the burro and Shep the dog (circa 1899), established tourist camp about 1890, later built trans-Canyon trail and cableway across river.

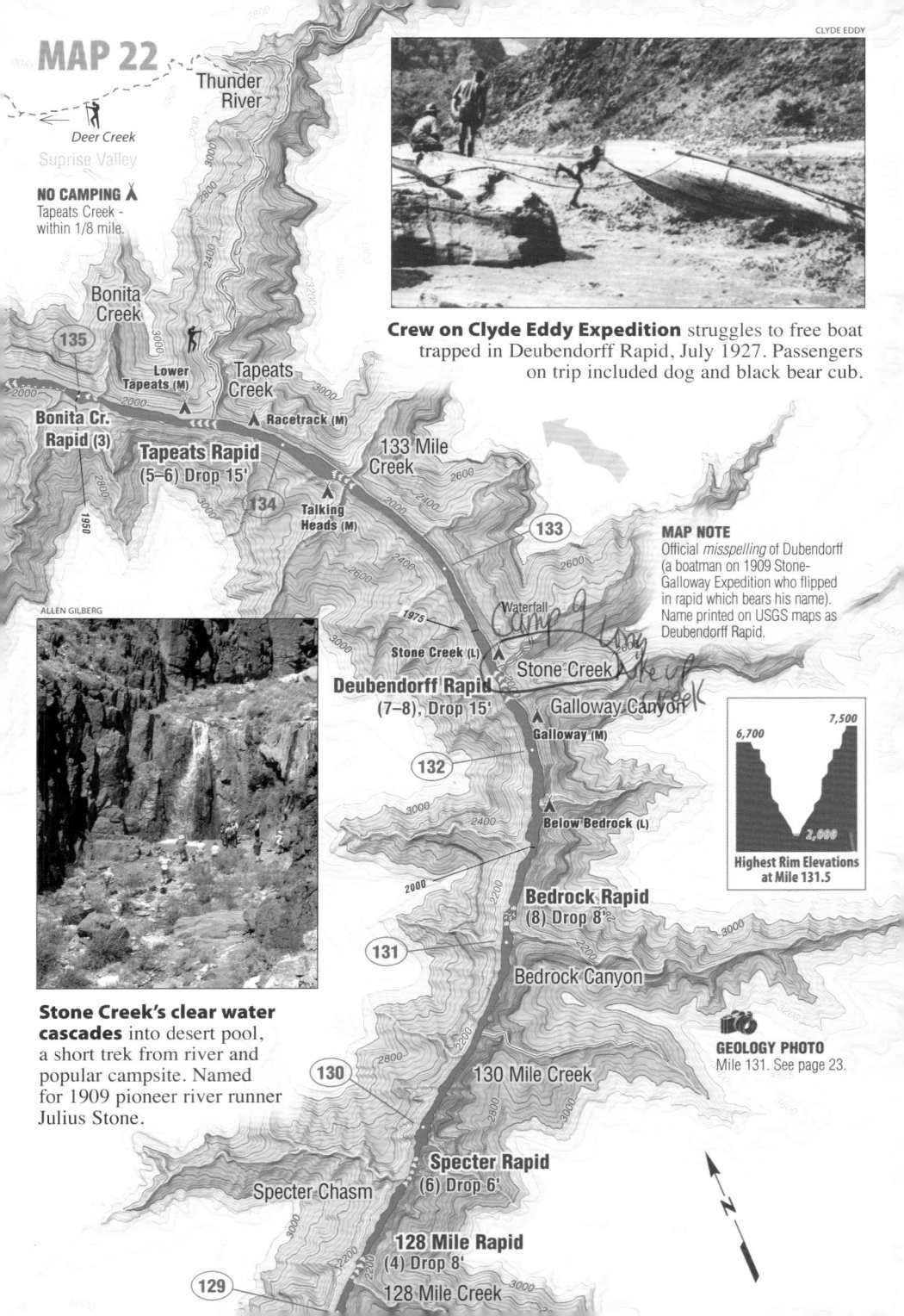

MAP 22

Thunder River

Deer Creek
Suprise Valley

NO CAMPING 𝕏
Tapeats Creek -
within 1/8 mile.

Bonita
Creek

135

**Bonita Cr.
Rapid (3)**

Tapeats Rapid
(5–6) Drop 15'

Lower
Tapeats (M)

Tapeats
Creek

Racetrack (M)

134

Talking
Heads (M)

133 Mile
Creek

133

Crew on Clyde Eddy Expedition struggles to free boat
trapped in Deubendorff Rapid, July 1927. Passengers
on trip included dog and black bear cub.

MAP NOTE
Official *misspelling* of Dubendorff
(a boatman on 1909 Stone-
Galloway Expedition who flipped
in rapid which bears his name).
Name printed on USGS maps as
Deubendorff Rapid.

ALLEN GILBERG

1975

Waterfall

Camp q log lake up creek

Stone Creek (L)

Stone Creek

Deubendorff Rapid
(7–8), Drop 15'

Galloway Canyon

Galloway (M)

132

Below Bedrock (L)

6,700	7,500

2,000

**Highest Rim Elevations
at Mile 131.5**

Bedrock Rapid
(8) Drop 8'

131

Bedrock Canyon

**Stone Creek's clear water
cascades** into desert pool,
a short trek from river and
popular campsite. Named
for 1909 pioneer river runner
Julius Stone.

130

130 Mile Creek

GEOLOGY PHOTO
Mile 131. See page 23.

Specter Rapid
(6) Drop 6'

Specter Chasm

128 Mile Rapid
(4) Drop 8'

129

128 Mile Creek

N

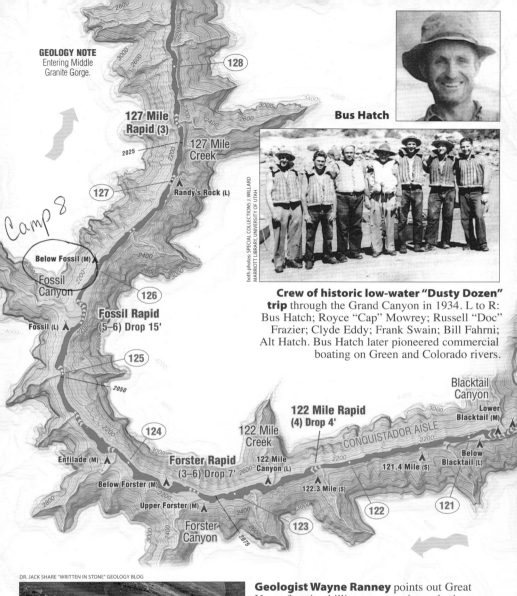

GEOLOGY NOTE
Entering Middle Granite Gorge.

127 Mile Rapid (3)

127 Mile Creek

Randy's Rock (L)

2025

127

Camp 8

Below Fossil (M)

Fossil Canyon

Fossil (L)

126

Fossil Rapid (5–6) Drop 15'

125

2050

124

Enfilade (M)

Below Forster (M)

Upper Forster (M)

Forster Rapid (3–6) Drop 7'

Forster Canyon

2075

123

122 Mile Creek

122 Mile Canyon (L)

122 Mile Rapid (4) Drop 4'

122.3 Mile (S)

122

121.4 Mile (S)

CONQUISTADOR AISLE

Blacktail Canyon

Lower Blacktail (M)

Below Blacktail (L)

121

Bus Hatch

Crew of historic low-water "Dusty Dozen" trip through the Grand Canyon in 1934. L to R: Bus Hatch; Royce "Cap" Mowrey; Russell "Doc" Frazier; Clyde Eddy; Frank Swain; Bill Fahrni; Alt Hatch. Bus Hatch later pioneered commercial boating on Green and Colorado rivers.

Geologist Wayne Ranney points out Great Unconformity, billion year gap in geologic history evident at Blacktail Canyon.

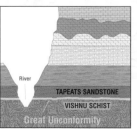

River

TAPEATS SANDSTONE

VISHNU SCHIST

Great Unconformity

GEOLOGY NOTE
Unconformities. See Geology pages 14 & 17.

MAP 21

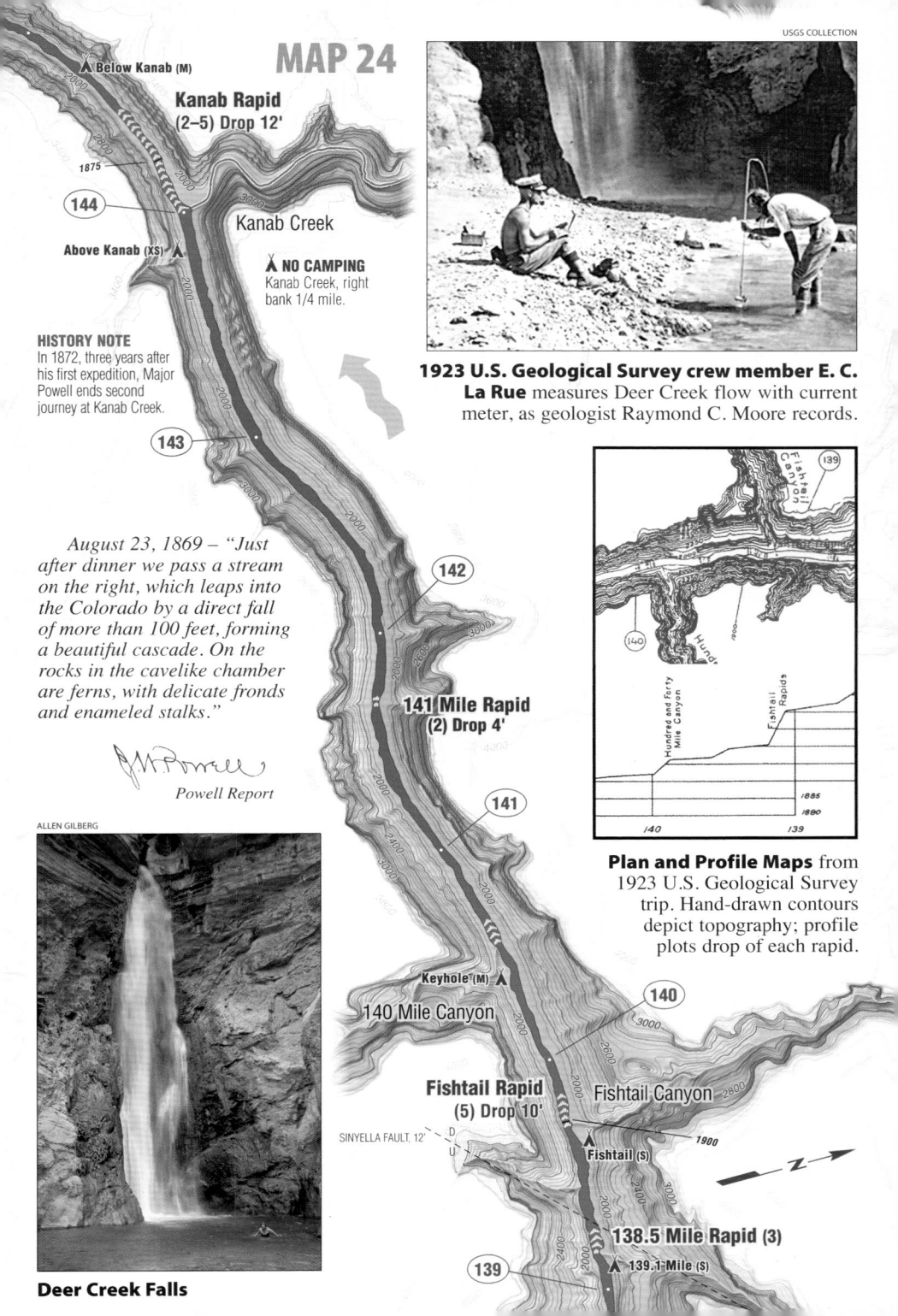

MAP 24

Below Kanab (M)

Kanab Rapid
(2–5) Drop 12'

1875

144

Above Kanab (XS)

Kanab Creek

NO CAMPING
Kanab Creek, right
bank 1/4 mile.

HISTORY NOTE
In 1872, three years after
his first expedition, Major
Powell ends second
journey at Kanab Creek.

143

*August 23, 1869 – "Just
after dinner we pass a stream
on the right, which leaps into
the Colorado by a direct fall
of more than 100 feet, forming
a beautiful cascade. On the
rocks in the cavelike chamber
are ferns, with delicate fronds
and enameled stalks."*

Powell Report

ALLEN GILBERG

Deer Creek Falls

142

141 Mile Rapid
(2) Drop 4'

141

Keyhole (M)

140 Mile Canyon

Fishtail Rapid
(5) Drop 10'

SINYELLA FAULT, 12"

Fishtail (S)

139

USGS COLLECTION

**1923 U.S. Geological Survey crew member E. C.
La Rue** measures Deer Creek flow with current
meter, as geologist Raymond C. Moore records.

139

140

Hundred and forty
Mile Canyon

Fishtail
Rapids

1885
1880

140   *139*

Plan and Profile Maps from
1923 U.S. Geological Survey
trip. Hand-drawn contours
depict topography; profile
plots drop of each rapid.

140

Fishtail Canyon

1900

138.5 Mile Rapid (3)

139.1 Mile (S)

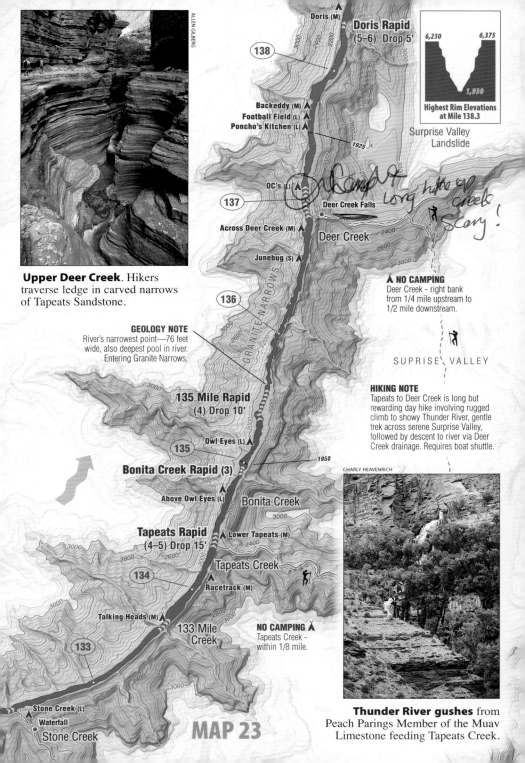

ALLEN GILBERG

Upper Deer Creek. Hikers traverse ledge in carved narrows of Tapeats Sandstone.

Doris (M)

Doris Rapid
(5–6) Drop 5'

138

6,250   6,375

1,930

Highest Rim Elevations at Mile 138.3

Surprise Valley Landslide

Backeddy (M)
Football Field (L)
Poncho's Kitchen (L)

1925

OC's (L)

Orange
long hike up
creek
scary!

137

Deer Creek Falls

Across Deer Creek (M)

Deer Creek

2400

Junebug (S)

2600

3000

NO CAMPING
Deer Creek - right bank from 1/4 mile upstream to 1/2 mile downstream.

136

SUPRISE VALLEY

GEOLOGY NOTE
River's narrowest point—76 feet wide, also deepest pool in river. Entering Granite Narrows.

GRANITE NARROWS

HIKING NOTE
Tapeats to Deer Creek is long but rewarding day hike involving rugged climb to showy Thunder River, gentle trek across serene Surprise Valley, followed by descent to river via Deer Creek drainage. Requires boat shuttle.

135 Mile Rapid
(4) Drop 10'

4064

135

Owl Eyes (L)

1950

CHARLY HEAVENRICH

Bonita Creek Rapid (3)

Above Owl Eyes (L)

Bonita Creek

3000

Tapeats Rapid
(4–5) Drop 15'

Lower Tapeats (M)

2400

134

Tapeats Creek

Racetrack (M)

Talking Heads (M)

133 Mile Creek

133

NO CAMPING
Tapeats Creek - within 1/8 mile.

2400

Stone Creek (L)
Waterfall
Stone Creek

MAP 23

Thunder River gushes from Peach Parings Member of the Muav Limestone feeding Tapeats Creek.

Havasu Falls drops into blue-green pool banked by spectacular travertine formations. Mineral-laden waters in Havasu Creek create vivid turquoise color that makes Havasupai famous. Best reached from Supai Village.

LOIE BELKNAP EVANS

MAP 26

ALLEN GILBERG

Dories line mouth of Havasu Creek—favorite hiking spot of river runners.

Second Chance (S)

159

1775

158.7 Mile (M)

First Chance (S)

158

Havasu Creek

Havasu Rapid
(2–4) Drop 3'

157

Very Last Chance (S)

ARCHAEOLOGY NOTE:
The Havasupai. See
Archaeology – page 94.

✗ NO CAMPING
Havasu Creek - left bank
100 yards upstream to
1/2 mile downstream.

HIKING NOTE:
Many river parties enjoy a stop to hike and splash in
Havasu Creek. Beaver Falls, 3.5 mile walk from river,
marks boundary with Havasupai tribal lands. Permit
required and fees apply: contact: 928-448-2121 or
www.havasupai-nsn.gov

Last Chance (M)

156

155

5,800	5,700

1,795

**Highest Rim Elevations
at Mile 156**

GEOLOGY PHOTO
Mile 155. See page 23.

MAP NOTE
Havasupai name
Sinyella is also
spelled Sinyala.

Sinyella Rapid
(2–3) Drop 2'

154

Havasupai ride in
rodeos, guide tourists,
farm the land on their
canyon reservation
reached by a 10-mile
trail from the rim.

153

Sinyella Canyon

BILL BELKNAP

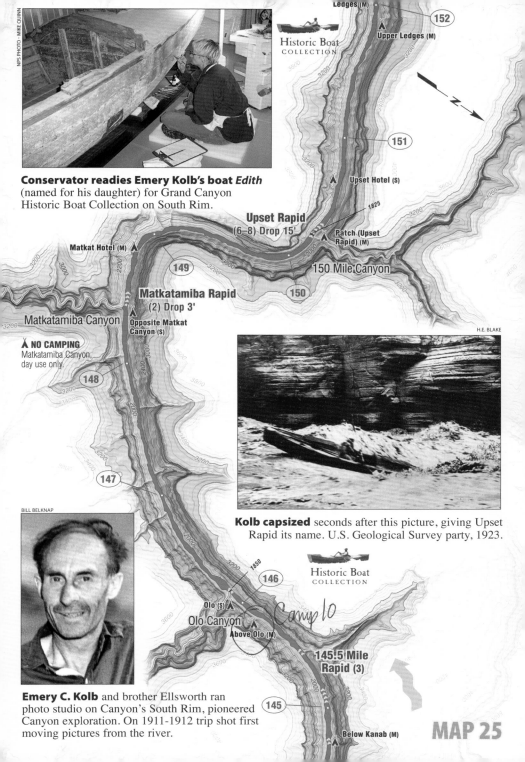

Conservator readies Emery Kolb's boat *Edith*
(named for his daughter) for Grand Canyon
Historic Boat Collection on South Rim.

Historic Boat
COLLECTION

Ledges (M)

⟨152⟩

Upper Ledges (M)

N

⟨151⟩

Upset Hotel (S)

1825

Upset Rapid
(6—8) Drop 15'

Patch (Upset
Rapid) (M)

Matkat Hotel (M)

⟨149⟩

150 Mile Canyon

Matkatamiba Rapid
(2) Drop 3'

⟨150⟩

Matkatamiba Canyon

Opposite Matkat
Canyon (S)

⚑ NO CAMPING
Matkatamiba Canyon,
day use only.

⟨148⟩

⟨147⟩

Kolb capsized seconds after this picture, giving Upset
Rapid its name. U.S. Geological Survey party, 1923.

Historic Boat
COLLECTION

1850

⟨146⟩

Olo (S)

Camp 10

Olo Canyon

Above Olo (M)

**145.5 Mile
Rapid** (3)

Emery C. Kolb and brother Ellsworth ran
photo studio on Canyon's South Rim, pioneered
Canyon exploration. On 1911-1912 trip shot first
moving pictures from the river.

⟨145⟩

Below Kanab (M)

MAP 25

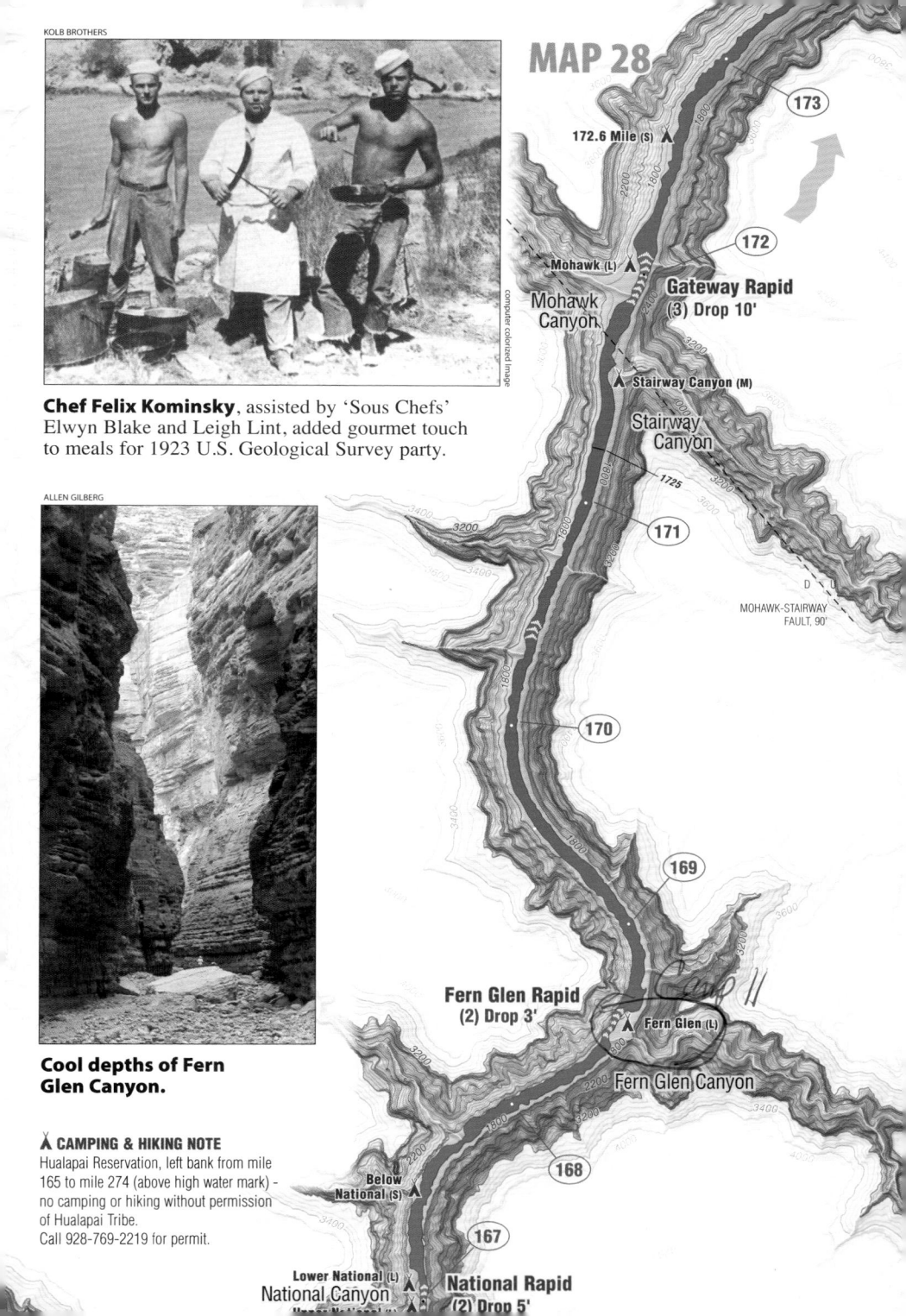

MAP 28

KOLB BROTHERS

Chef Felix Kominsky, assisted by 'Sous Chefs' Elwyn Blake and Leigh Lint, added gourmet touch to meals for 1923 U.S. Geological Survey party.

ALLEN GILBERG

Cool depths of Fern Glen Canyon.

Ⅹ **CAMPING & HIKING NOTE**
Hualapai Reservation, left bank from mile 165 to mile 274 (above high water mark) - no camping or hiking without permission of Hualapai Tribe.
Call 928-769-2219 for permit.

173

172.6 Mile (S)

172

Mohawk (L)

Gateway Rapid
(3) Drop 10'

Mohawk Canyon

Stairway Canyon (M)

Stairway Canyon

1725

171

MOHAWK-STAIRWAY FAULT, 90'

170

169

Fern Glen Rapid
(2) Drop 3'

Fern Glen (L)

Fern Glen Canyon

168

Below National (S)

167

Lower National (L)

National Canyon

National Rapid
(2) Drop 5'

computer colorized image

HUALAPAI
RESERVATION

GRAND
CANYON
NATIONAL
PARK

**Rod Sanderson and
Jim Jordan** drove first
outboard motors through
Canyon, June 1951.

166

▲ 165.7 Mile (S)

Below Tuckup (S) ▲

164 Mile Rapid
(2) Drop 4'

1750

165

▲ Tuckup (L)

▲ Above Tuckup (S)

Tuckup Canyon

N

5,800   5,900

1,745

**Highest Rim Elevations
at Mile 165.7**

164

*"Our rations are still spoiling; the
bacon is so badly injured that we throw
it away. We have now only musty flour
sufficient for ten days and a few dried
apples, but plenty of coffee…We may be
compelled to give up the expedition."*

Powell Report

163

162

161

▲ 161.3 Mile (S)

▲ 160.5 Mile (S)

160

MAP 27

Girls grill golden brown pork chops where
Powell party stretched meager rations.

MAP 30

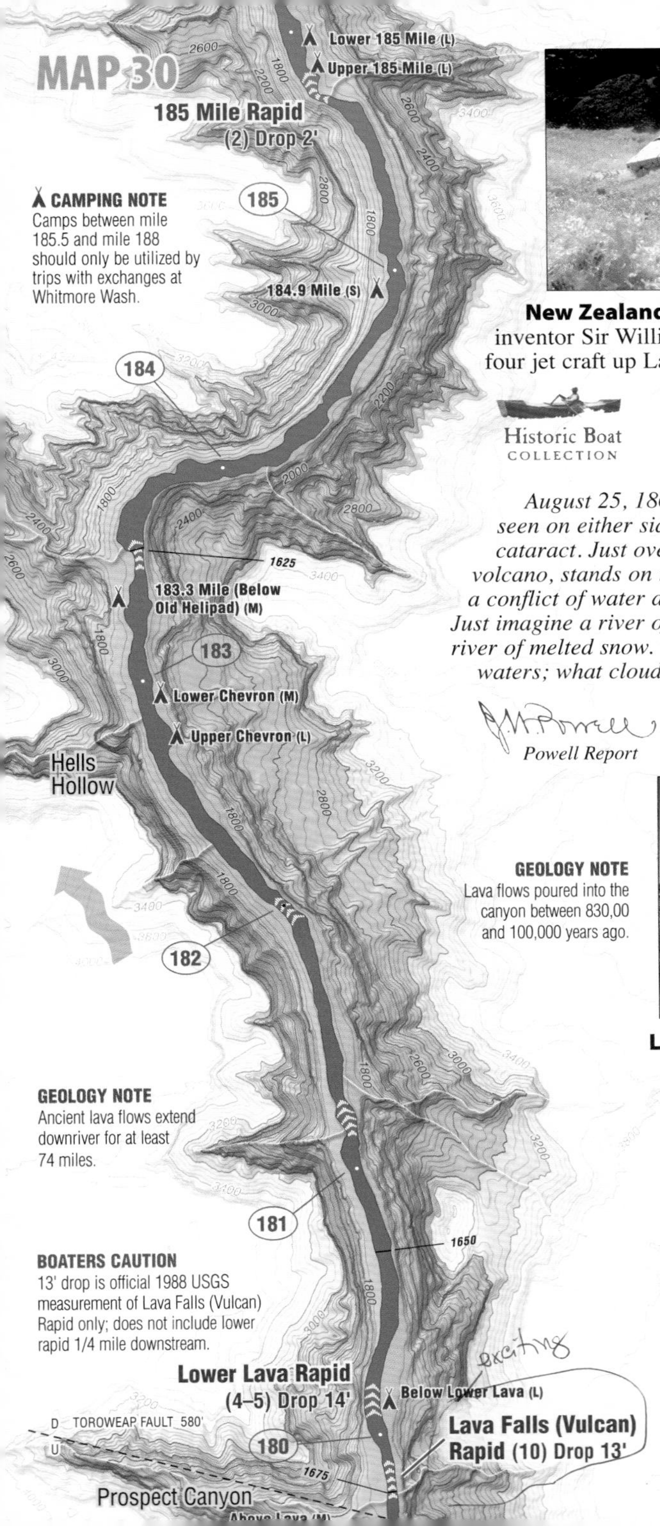

Lower 185 Mile (L)
Upper 185 Mile (L)

185 Mile Rapid
(2) Drop 2'

185

CAMPING NOTE
Camps between mile
185.5 and mile 188
should only be utilized by
trips with exchanges at
Whitmore Wash.

184.9 Mile (S)

184

183.3 Mile (Below
Old Helipad) (M)

183

Lower Chevron (M)

Upper Chevron (L)

Hells
Hollow

182

GEOLOGY NOTE
Ancient lava flows extend
downriver for at least
74 miles.

181

BOATERS CAUTION
13' drop is official 1988 USGS
measurement of Lava Falls (Vulcan)
Rapid only; does not include lower
rapid 1/4 mile downstream.

exciting

Lower Lava Rapid
(4–5) Drop 14'

Below Lower Lava (L)

D   TOROWEAP FAULT 580'

U

180

Lava Falls (Vulcan)
Rapid (10) Drop 13'

Prospect Canyon

BILL BELKNAP

New Zealander Jon Hamilton, son of jet boat
inventor Sir William Hamilton, successfully piloted
four jet craft up Lava Falls during 1960 uprun of the
Colorado. *Wee Red* shown above.

Historic Boat
COLLECTION

*August 25, 1869 – "Great Quantities of lava are
seen on either side; and then we come to an abrupt
cataract. Just over the fall a cinder cone, or extinct
volcano, stands on the very brink of the canyon. What
a conflict of water and fire there must have been here!
Just imagine a river of molten rock running down into a
river of melted snow. What a seething and boiling of the
waters; what clouds of steam rolled into the heavens!*

"Thirty-five miles today. Hurrah!"

Powell Report

GEOLOGY NOTE
Lava flows poured into the
canyon between 830,00
and 100,000 years ago.

WAYNE RANNEY

Paleozoic bedrock

Lava filled channel

Lava filled channel at Mile 183.3.

Vulcan's Anvil, a volcanic
remnant, towers in river a
mile above Lava Falls. Native
Americans prefer that sacred
site remain untouched.

Highest Rim Elevations at Mile 179

6,400   6,400

1,675

GEOLOGY NOTE
Vulcan's Anvil, a 50-foot lava plug signaling the approach of Lava Falls, is what remains of a volcano that erupted about 200,000 years ago.

GEOLOGY NOTE
The Lavas. See Geology page 13.

Vulcan's Anvil

Above Anvil (L)

Toroweap Overlook   EL 4520

Honga Spring (M)

178

177

HUALAPAI RESERVATION

Otis "Dock" Marston drives racing Chris Craft through Lava Falls on June 1950 Hudson-Marston trip.

BILL BELKNAP

Saddle Horse Canyon

GRAND CANYON NATIONAL PARK

1934 "Dusty Dozen" crew shows grit in tricky low water lining of Lava Falls on approximately 1600 c.f.s. Crew member Doc Frazier inspired quest to place plaque at Separation Canyon honoring three men killed after leaving first Powell Expedition. He hired Bus Hatch and Frank Swain of Vernal, Utah, to run boats through Canyon. (See Map 39).

Below Red Slide (L)

176

Red Slide

1700

175

Lower Cove (L)

Upper Cove (S)

Cove Canyon

SPECIAL COLLECTIONS J. WILLARD MARRIOTT LIBRARY, UNIVERSITY OF UTAH

GEOLOGY PHOTO
Mile 174. See page 24.

174

173

MAP 29

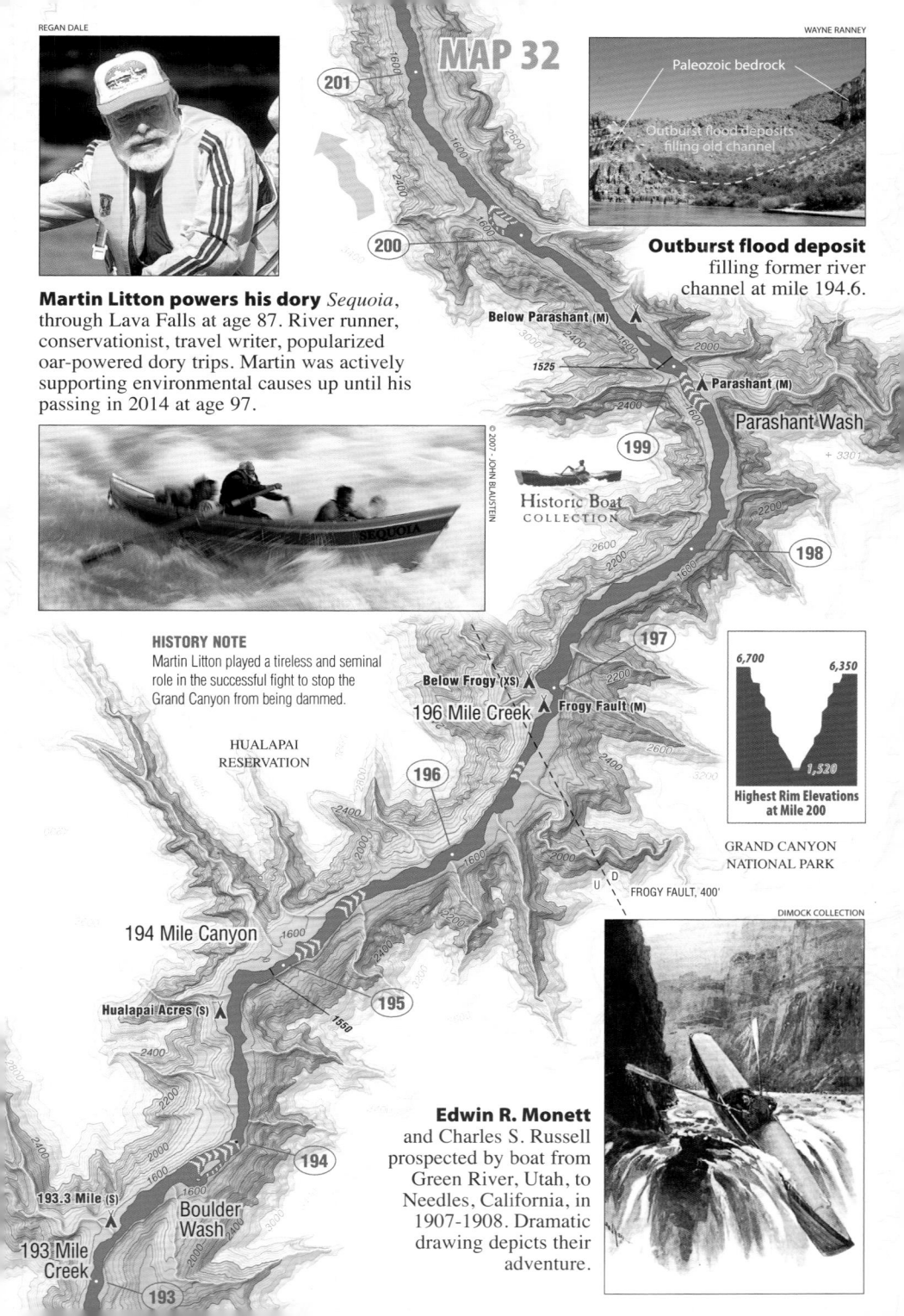

REGAN DALE

WAYNE RANNEY

MAP 32

201

200

Paleozoic bedrock

Outburst flood deposits
filling old channel

Outburst flood deposit
filling former river
channel at mile 194.6.

Martin Litton powers his dory *Sequoia*,
through Lava Falls at age 87. River runner,
conservationist, travel writer, popularized
oar-powered dory trips. Martin was actively
supporting environmental causes up until his
passing in 2014 at age 97.

© 2007 - JOHN BLAUSTEIN

Below Parashant (M)

1525

Parashant (M)

Parashant Wash

199

+ 3301

Historic Boat
COLLECTION

198

197

HISTORY NOTE
Martin Litton played a tireless and seminal
role in the successful fight to stop the
Grand Canyon from being dammed.

Below Frogy (XS)

196 Mile Creek

Frogy Fault (M)

6,700   6,350

196

1,520

**HUALAPAI
RESERVATION**

**Highest Rim Elevations
at Mile 200**

**GRAND CANYON
NATIONAL PARK**

U   D

FROGY FAULT, 400'

DIMOCK COLLECTION

194 Mile Canyon

195

Hualapai Acres (S)

194

193.3 Mile (S)

Edwin R. Monett
and Charles S. Russell
prospected by boat from
Green River, Utah, to
Needles, California, in
1907-1908. Dramatic
drawing depicts their
adventure.

**Boulder
Wash**

193 Mile
Creek

193

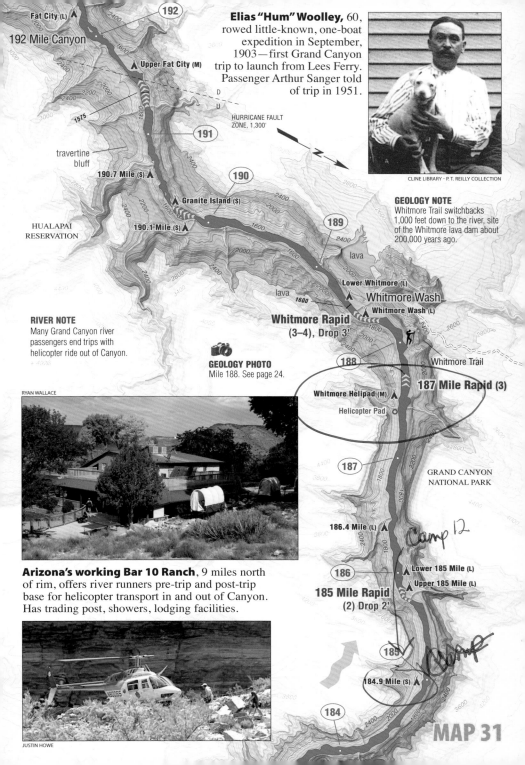

Fat City (L)

192 Mile Canyon

192

Upper Fat City (M)

1575

HURRICANE FAULT
ZONE, 1,300'

191

travertine
bluff

190.7 Mile (S)

190

Granite Island (S)

189

190.1 Mile (S)

HUALAPAI
RESERVATION

lava

GEOLOGY NOTE
Whitmore Trail switchbacks
1,000 feet down to the river, site
of the Whitmore lava dam about
200,000 years ago.

lava

Lower Whitmore (L)

Whitmore Wash

Whitmore Wash (L)

RIVER NOTE
Many Grand Canyon river
passengers end trips with
helicopter ride out of Canyon.

Whitmore Rapid
(3–4), Drop 3'

GEOLOGY PHOTO
Mile 188. See page 24.

188

Whitmore Trail

187 Mile Rapid (3)

Whitmore Helipad (M)

Helicopter Pad

RYAN WALLACE

187

GRAND CANYON
NATIONAL PARK

Camp 12

186.4 Mile (L)

Arizona's working Bar 10 Ranch, 9 miles north
of rim, offers river runners pre-trip and post-trip
base for helicopter transport in and out of Canyon.
Has trading post, showers, lodging facilities.

186

Lower 185 Mile (L)

Upper 185 Mile (L)

185 Mile Rapid
(2) Drop 2'

Camp

185

184.9 Mile (S)

184

MAP 31

JUSTIN HOWE

Elias "Hum" Woolley, 60,
rowed little-known, one-boat
expedition in September,
1903—first Grand Canyon
trip to launch from Lees Ferry.
Passenger Arthur Sanger told
of trip in 1951.

CLINE LIBRARY - P. T. REILLY COLLECTION

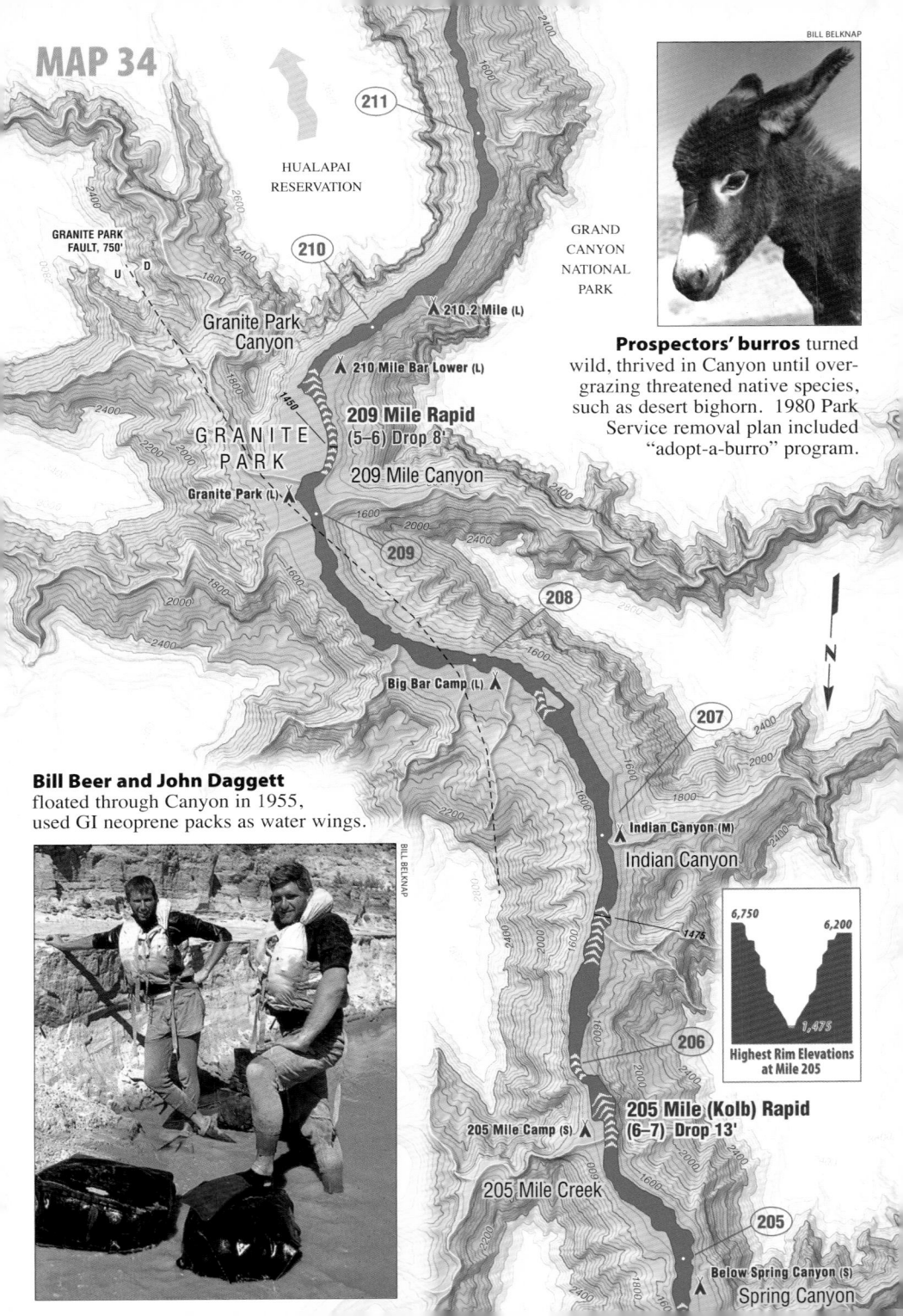

MAP 34

211

HUALAPAI
RESERVATION

210

GRAND
CANYON
NATIONAL
PARK

GRANITE PARK
FAULT, 750'

U   D

Granite Park
Canyon

210.2 Mile (L)

210 Mile Bar Lower (L)

1450

209 Mile Rapid
(5–6) Drop 8'

G R A N I T E
P A R K

209 Mile Canyon

Granite Park (L)

209

208

BILL BELKNAP

Prospectors' burros turned
wild, thrived in Canyon until over-
grazing threatened native species,
such as desert bighorn. 1980 Park
Service removal plan included
"adopt-a-burro" program.

N

Big Bar Camp (L)

207

Indian Canyon (M)

Indian Canyon

1476

Bill Beer and John Daggett
floated through Canyon in 1955,
used GI neoprene packs as water wings.

BILL BELKNAP

6,750   6,200

1,473

**Highest Rim Elevations
at Mile 205**

206

205 Mile Camp (S)

205 Mile (Kolb) Rapid
(6–7) Drop 13'

205 Mile Creek

205

Below Spring Canyon (S)

Spring Canyon

Crew members Buzz Belknap and Ed I'Anson aboard jet boat "Dock" July 1960. Belknap, age 16, piloted craft up majority of rapids on historic uprun of Colorado.

BILL BELKNAP

BILL BELKNAP

Historic Boat
COLLECTION

204

203

▲ 203 Mile (M)

1500

≋ ▲ 202 Mile (M)

202

201

HISTORY NOTE
See page 31 for more information on river legend Georgie White Clark.

River running pioneers Georgie White Clark and Harry Aleson teamed up on one-man raft at mouth of Parashant Creek (Mile 198.5) June 1946; then floated to Lake Mead. Aleson explored idea of power-boat upruns of the river in 1940s, made it from Lake Mead to foot of 217 Mile Rapid in October 1943.

200

▲ Below Parashant (M)

1525

198   199

≋ ▲ Parashant (L)

Parashant Wash

BILL BELKNAP

MAP 33

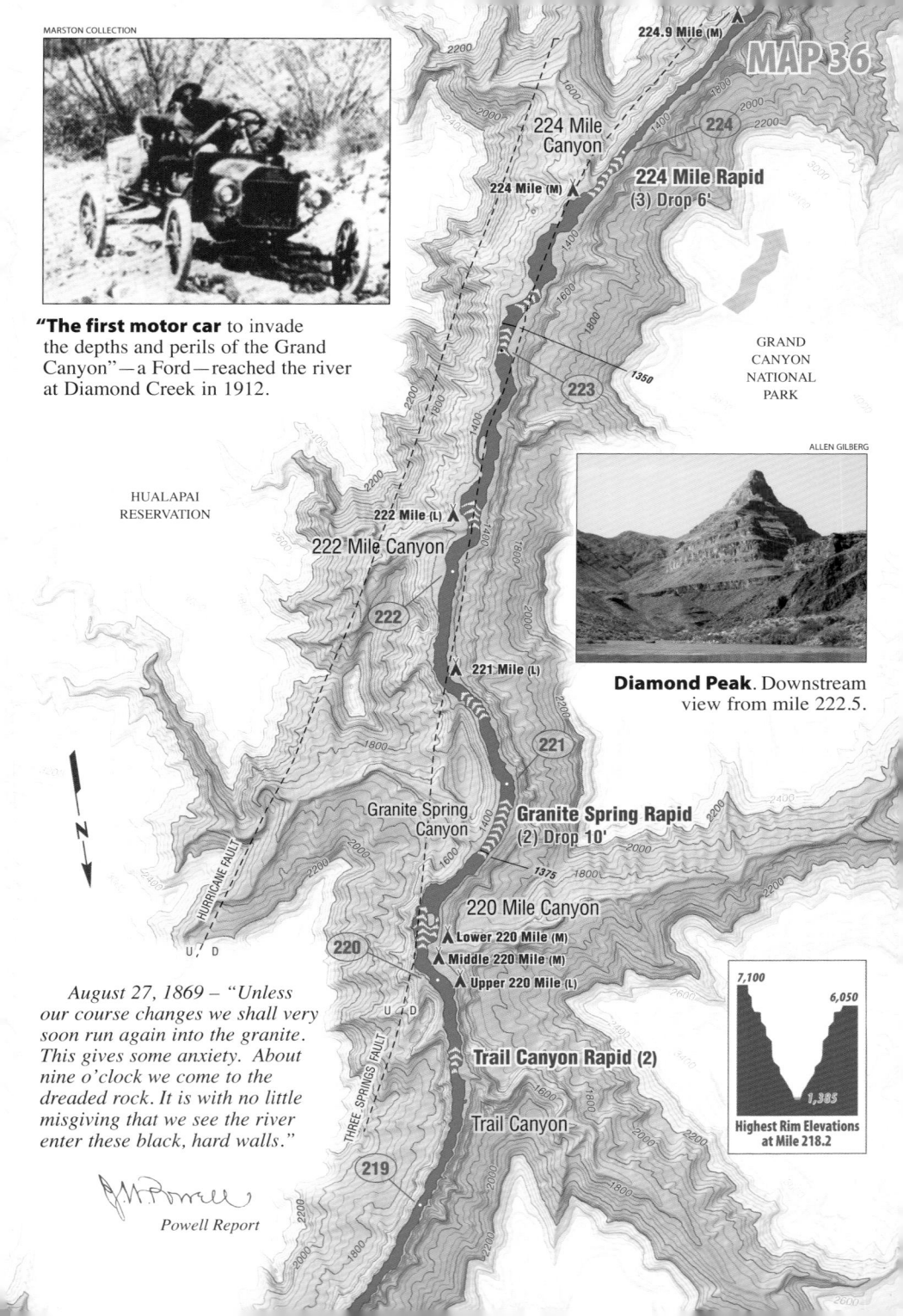

MAP 36

MARSTON COLLECTION

224.9 Mile (M)

2200

1600

1800

1400

2000

2200

224

224 Mile
Canyon

224 Mile (M)

224 Mile Rapid
(3) Drop 6'

1400

1800

3000

1600

GRAND
CANYON
NATIONAL
PARK

"The first motor car to invade
the depths and perils of the Grand
Canyon"—a Ford—reached the river
at Diamond Creek in 1912.

223

1350

2200

1800

1400

ALLEN GILBERG

HUALAPAI
RESERVATION

2200

222 Mile (L)

222 Mile Canyon

1400

1800

222

2000

2200

Diamond Peak. Downstream
view from mile 222.5.

221 Mile (L)

2200

221

1800

Granite Spring
Canyon

Granite Spring Rapid
(2) Drop 10'

2000

2400

1400

1375

1800

220 Mile Canyon

2200

1600

Lower 220 Mile (M)

Middle 220 Mile (M)

Upper 220 Mile (L)

220

U / D

*August 27, 1869 – "Unless
our course changes we shall very
soon run again into the granite.
This gives some anxiety. About
nine o'clock we come to the
dreaded rock. It is with no little
misgiving that we see the river
enter these black, hard walls."*

HURRICANE FAULT

THREE SPRINGS FAULT

U / D

Trail Canyon Rapid (2)

Trail Canyon

219

2200

1800

2000

1800

7,100

6,050

1,385

**Highest Rim Elevations
at Mile 218.2**

J.W. Powell

Powell Report

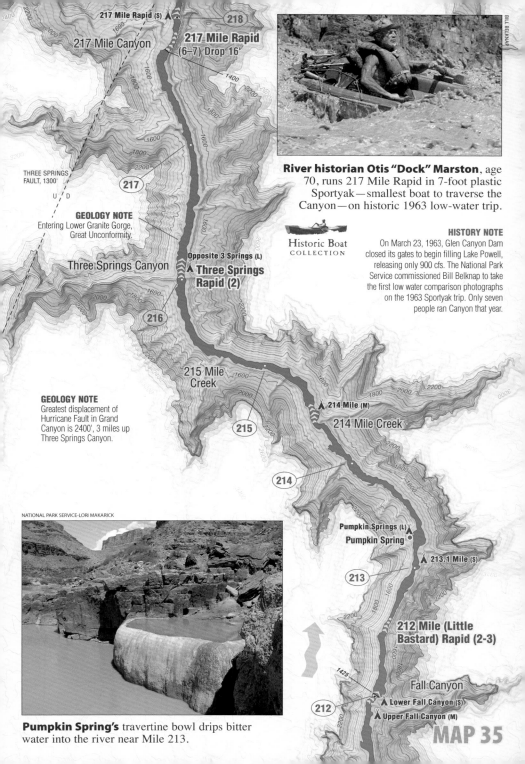

217 Mile Rapid (S)

218

217 Mile Rapid
(6–7) Drop 16'

217 Mile Canyon

217

THREE SPRINGS
FAULT, 1300'

U / D

GEOLOGY NOTE
Entering Lower Granite Gorge,
Great Unconformity.

Three Springs Canyon

Opposite 3 Springs (L)
Three Springs
Rapid (2)

216

GEOLOGY NOTE
Greatest displacement of
Hurricane Fault in Grand
Canyon is 2400', 3 miles up
Three Springs Canyon.

215 Mile
Creek

215

214 Mile (M)

214 Mile Creek

214

BILL BELKNAP

River historian Otis "Dock" Marston, age
70, runs 217 Mile Rapid in 7-foot plastic
Sportyak—smallest boat to traverse the
Canyon—on historic 1963 low-water trip.

Historic Boat
COLLECTION

HISTORY NOTE
On March 23, 1963, Glen Canyon Dam
closed its gates to begin filling Lake Powell,
releasing only 900 cfs. The National Park
Service commissioned Bill Belknap to take
the first low water comparison photographs
on the 1963 Sportyak trip. Only seven
people ran Canyon that year.

NATIONAL PARK SERVICE-LORI MAKARICK

Pumpkin Springs (L)
Pumpkin Spring

213.1 Mile (S)

213

212 Mile (Little
Bastard) Rapid (2-3)

1425

Fall Canyon

212

Lower Fall Canyon (S)

Upper Fall Canyon (M)

Pumpkin Spring's travertine bowl drips bitter
water into the river near Mile 213.

MAP 35

MAP 38

Derelict sweepscow was found floating near Mile 237 with Hydes' belongings aboard, including Bessie's camera and notebook.

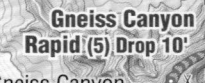
Gneiss Canyon Rapid (5) Drop 10'

Gneiss Canyon

Gneiss Canyon (M)

1225

Bridge Canyon (M)

Bridge Canyon

235.1 Mile (S)

236

Bridge Canyon Rapid (3–5) Drop 10'

235

234.4 Mile (S)

234

234 Mile Rapid (4–6) Drop 5'

Author/historian Brad Dimock and Jeri Ledbetter during reenactment of 1928 Bride and Groom trip, aboard replica of Glen Hyde's 'sweepscow.' Hands-on research led to Dimock's book, *Sunk Without a Sound.* www.fretwater.com

233

232 Mile **Rapid** (4–7) Drop 7'

1250

232

— N →

231

231 Mile Rapid (4–7) Drop 12'

Travertine Falls

231 Mile (S)

Travertine Falls formed gradually as mineral-rich spring water evaporated, depositing calcium carbonate—just like scale deposits inside a tea kettle.

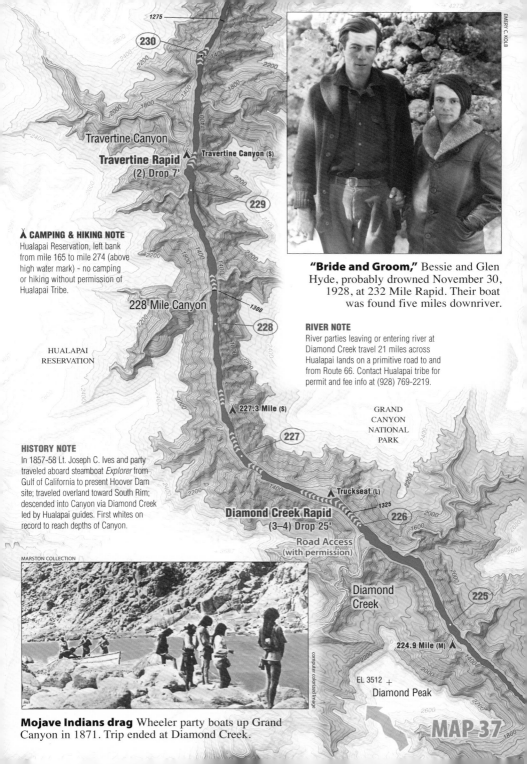

1275

230

Travertine Canyon

Travertine Rapid ⚲ Travertine Canyon (S)
(2) Drop 7'

229

✕ **CAMPING & HIKING NOTE**
Hualapai Reservation, left bank
from mile 165 to mile 274 (above
high water mark) - no camping
or hiking without permission of
Hualapai Tribe.

228 Mile Canyon

228

HUALAPAI
RESERVATION

1300

1275

EMERY C. KOLB

"Bride and Groom," Bessie and Glen
Hyde, probably drowned November 30,
1928, at 232 Mile Rapid. Their boat
was found five miles downriver.

RIVER NOTE
River parties leaving or entering river at
Diamond Creek travel 21 miles across
Hualapai lands on a primitive road to and
from Route 66. Contact Hualapai tribe for
permit and fee info at (928) 769-2219.

⚲ 227.3 Mile (S)

227

GRAND
CANYON
NATIONAL
PARK

HISTORY NOTE
In 1857-58 Lt. Joseph C. Ives and party
traveled aboard steamboat *Explorer* from
Gulf of California to present Hoover Dam
site; traveled overland toward South Rim;
descended into Canyon via Diamond Creek
led by Hualapai guides. First whites on
record to reach depths of Canyon.

⚲ Truckseat (L)
1325

Diamond Creek Rapid
(3–4) Drop 25'
226

Road Access
(with permission)

Diamond
Creek

225

224.9 Mile (M) ⚲

computer colorized image

EL 3512 +
Diamond Peak

MARSTON COLLECTION

Mojave Indians drag Wheeler party boats up Grand
Canyon in 1871. Trip ended at Diamond Creek.

⭐ MAP 37

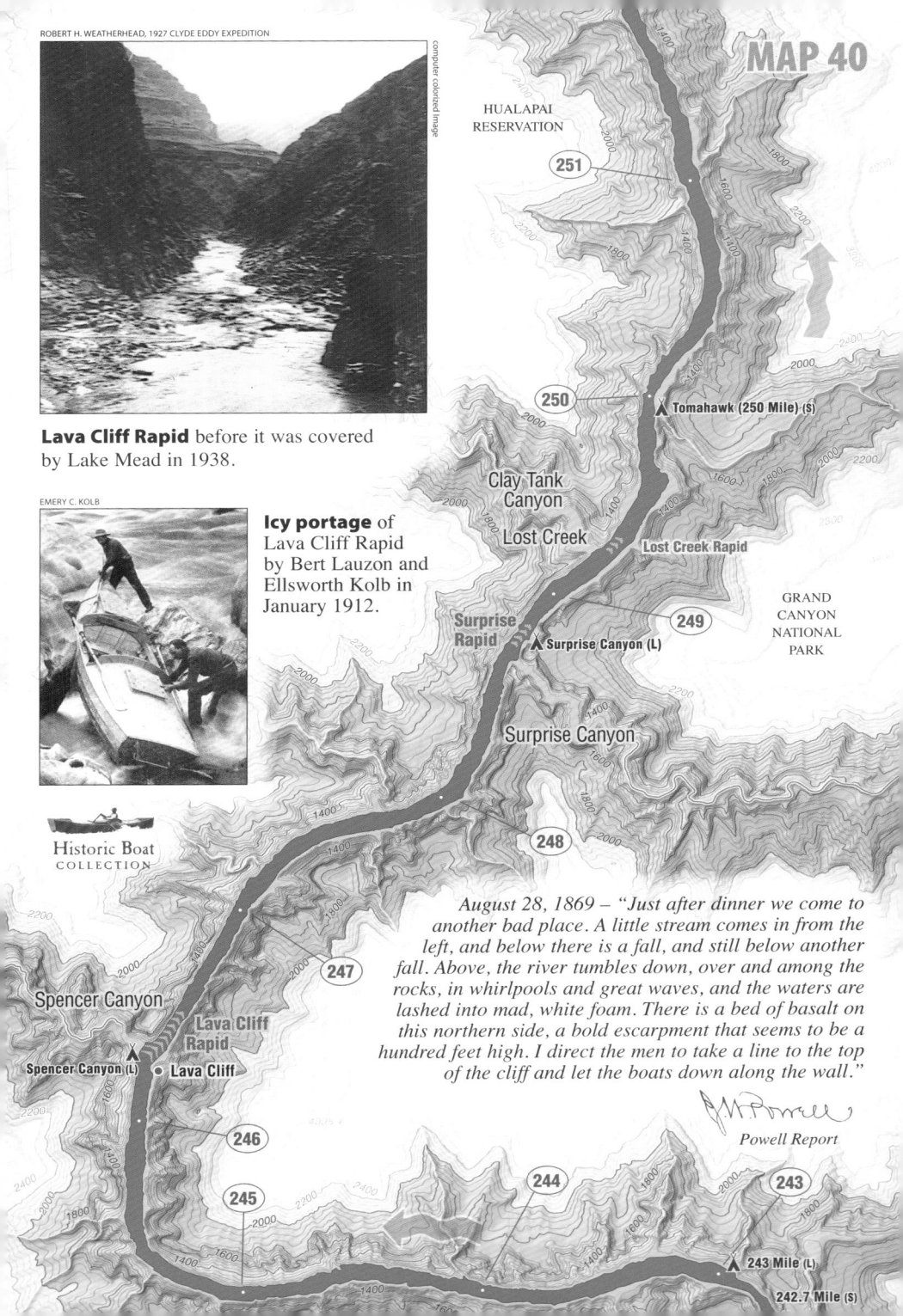

ROBERT H. WEATHERHEAD, 1927 CLYDE EDDY EXPEDITION

computer colorized image

Lava Cliff Rapid before it was covered by Lake Mead in 1938.

EMERY C. KOLB

Icy portage of Lava Cliff Rapid by Bert Lauzon and Ellsworth Kolb in January 1912.

Historic Boat
COLLECTION

MAP 40

HUALAPAI
RESERVATION

251

250

Tomahawk (250 Mile) (S)

Clay Tank
Canyon

Lost Creek

Lost Creek Rapid

**Surprise
Rapid**

Surprise Canyon (L)

249

GRAND
CANYON
NATIONAL
PARK

Surprise Canyon

248

247

Spencer Canyon

**Lava Cliff
Rapid**

Spencer Canyon (L)   Lava Cliff

246

245   244   243

243 Mile (L)

242.7 Mile (S)

August 28, 1869 – "Just after dinner we come to another bad place. A little stream comes in from the left, and below there is a fall, and still below another fall. Above, the river tumbles down, over and among the rocks, in whirlpools and great waves, and the waters are lashed into mad, white foam. There is a bed of basalt on this northern side, a bold escarpment that seems to be a hundred feet high. I direct the men to take a line to the top of the cliff and let the boats down along the wall."

Powell Report

August 28, 1869 – *"We come to a place which seems worse than any yet; to run it would be sure destruction. After supper Captain Howland asks to talk with me. He, his brother, and William Dunn have determined to go no farther. All night long I pace up and down. Is it wise to go on? At last daylight comes; breakfast is as solemn as a funeral. Two rifles and a shotgun are given to the men who are going out. I ask them to help themselves to rations. They refuse, but Billy the cook has a pan of biscuits for dinner, and these he leaves on a rock. Some tears are shed; each party thinks the other is taking the dangerous course.*

The three men watch us off. We are scarcely a minute in running it; we have passed many places that were worse. We wait until their coming seems hopeless, and then push on."

Powell Report

GEOLOGY NOTE
The Colorado River deposits silt as current is slowed by Lake Mead. Rapids now buried by silt are shown in gray.

SEPARATION FAULT, 210'

HISTORY NOTE
Buzz Holmstrom, on solo run in 1937, and Carnegie-Cal Tech geological study group were last to see Separation and Lava Cliff rapids before their submersion by Lake Mead. Upstream, at Diamond Creek, the Holmstrom-Carnegie Tech parties were the first to cross paths in Canyon.

HISTORY NOTE
Bridge Canyon Dam, a hydropower project first proposed in 1920, was seriously considered until 1968 when persistent public opinion defeated proposal. Dam would have stood 740 feet high and backed up reservoir nearly 93 miles in Grand Canyon.

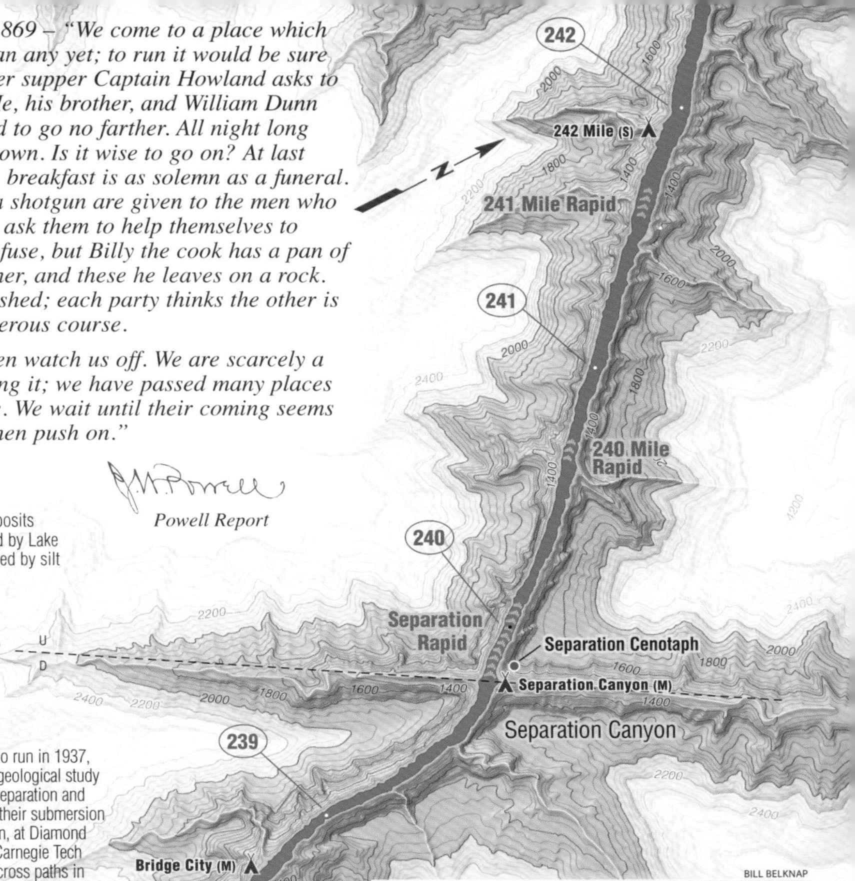

Proposed Historic Bridge Canyon Dam Site

237 Mile Rapid

MAP 39

242

242 Mile (S)

241 Mile Rapid

241

240 Mile Rapid

240

Separation Rapid

Separation Cenotaph

Separation Canyon (M)

Separation Canyon

239

Bridge City (M)

238

237

236.7 Mile (S)

BILL BELKNAP

HERE · ON · AUGUST · 28
1869
SENECA · HOWLAND, O.G. HOWLAND,
AND
WILLIAM · H. DUNN
SEPARATED · FROM · THE · ORIGINAL
POWELL · PARTY, · CLIMBED · TO
THE · NORTH · RIM · AND · WERE
KILLED · BY · THE · INDIANS.

FOR · FURTHER · AUTHENTIC
INFORMATION · SEE · "COLORADO
RIVER · CONTROVERSIES"
OBTAINABLE · FROM · UNIVERSITY
LIBRARIES.

THIS · CENOTAPH · WAS · PLACED
AND · DEDICATED · IN · 1939 · BY · LATER
COLORADO · RIVER · VOYAGERS.

Bronze *cenotaph* (Greek for "empty tomb") at Separation Canyon honors trio who left Powell's party at this point.

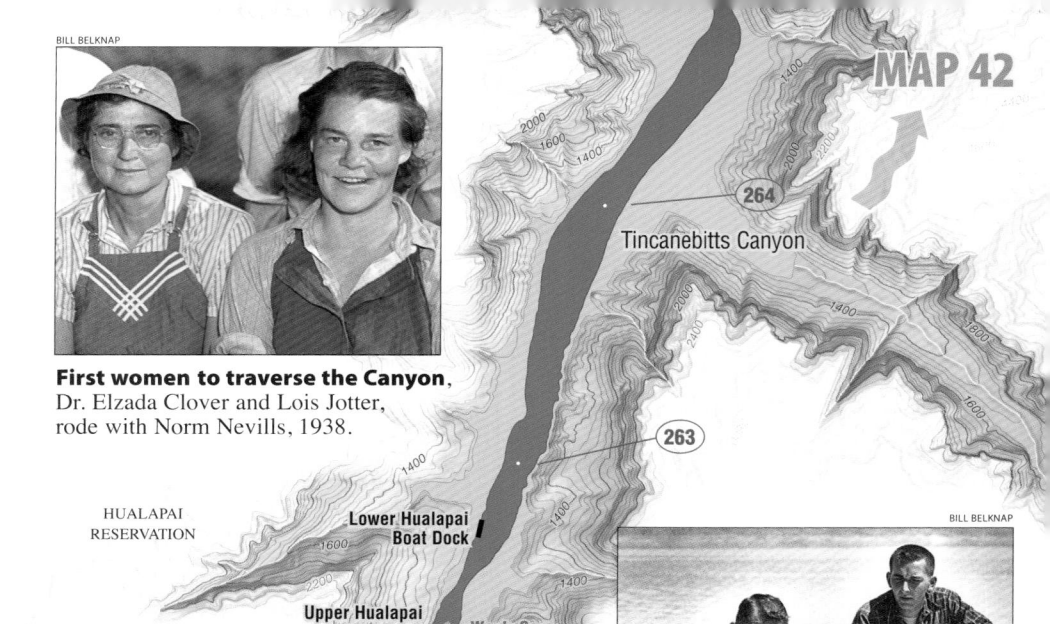

MAP 42

264

Tincanebitts Canyon

First women to traverse the Canyon,
Dr. Elzada Clover and Lois Jotter,
rode with Norm Nevills, 1938.

263

HUALAPAI
RESERVATION

Lower Hualapai
Boat Dock

Upper Hualapai
Boat Dock

Wards Cave
Rapid

262

HISTORY NOTE
June 1983, Kenton Grua, Rudi
Petschek, and Steve Reynolds in
dory *Emerald Mile*, set new speed
record from Lees Ferry to Grand
Wash Fault of 36:38:29 on 72,000
c.f.s. in spite of an upset and righting
at Crystal Rapid. This adventure was
the inspiration for Kevin Fedarko's
award-winning book—*The Emerald
Mile: The Epic Story of the Fastest
Ride in History Through the Heart
of the Grand Canyon.*

MEXICAN HAT

Jim and Bob Rigg set speed record
in 1951 rowing a Nevills cataract boat
through Canyon in two-and a half-days.

261

260

Lower Quartermaster

Emerald Mile—Triumphant Trio
Rudi Petschek, Kenton Grua and
Steve Reynolds (left to right,
see History Note above).

Waterfall
Rapid

Quartermaster
Canyon

Burnt Spring Canyon

259

**GEOLOGY
NOTE**
Travertine bluff
formed at lake
level from
ancient spring.

GRAND
CANYON
NATIONAL
PARK

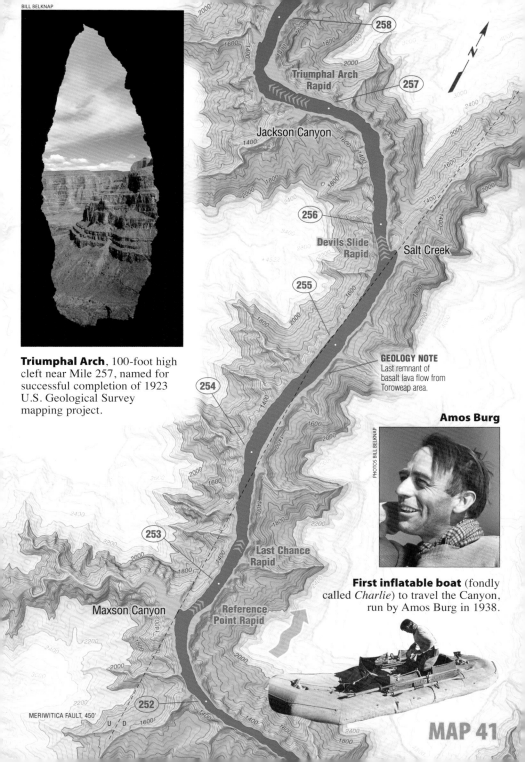

BILL BELKNAP

Triumphal Arch, 100-foot high cleft near Mile 257, named for successful completion of 1923 U.S. Geological Survey mapping project.

258

Triumphal Arch Rapid

257

Jackson Canyon

1400

256

Devils Slide Rapid

Salt Creek

255

GEOLOGY NOTE
Last remnant of basalt lava flow from Toroweap area.

254

Amos Burg

PHOTOS BILL BELKNAP

253

Last Chance Rapid

First inflatable boat (fondly called *Charlie*) to travel the Canyon, run by Amos Burg in 1938.

Maxson Canyon

Reference Point Rapid

252

MERIWITICA FAULT, 450'

U   D

MAP 41

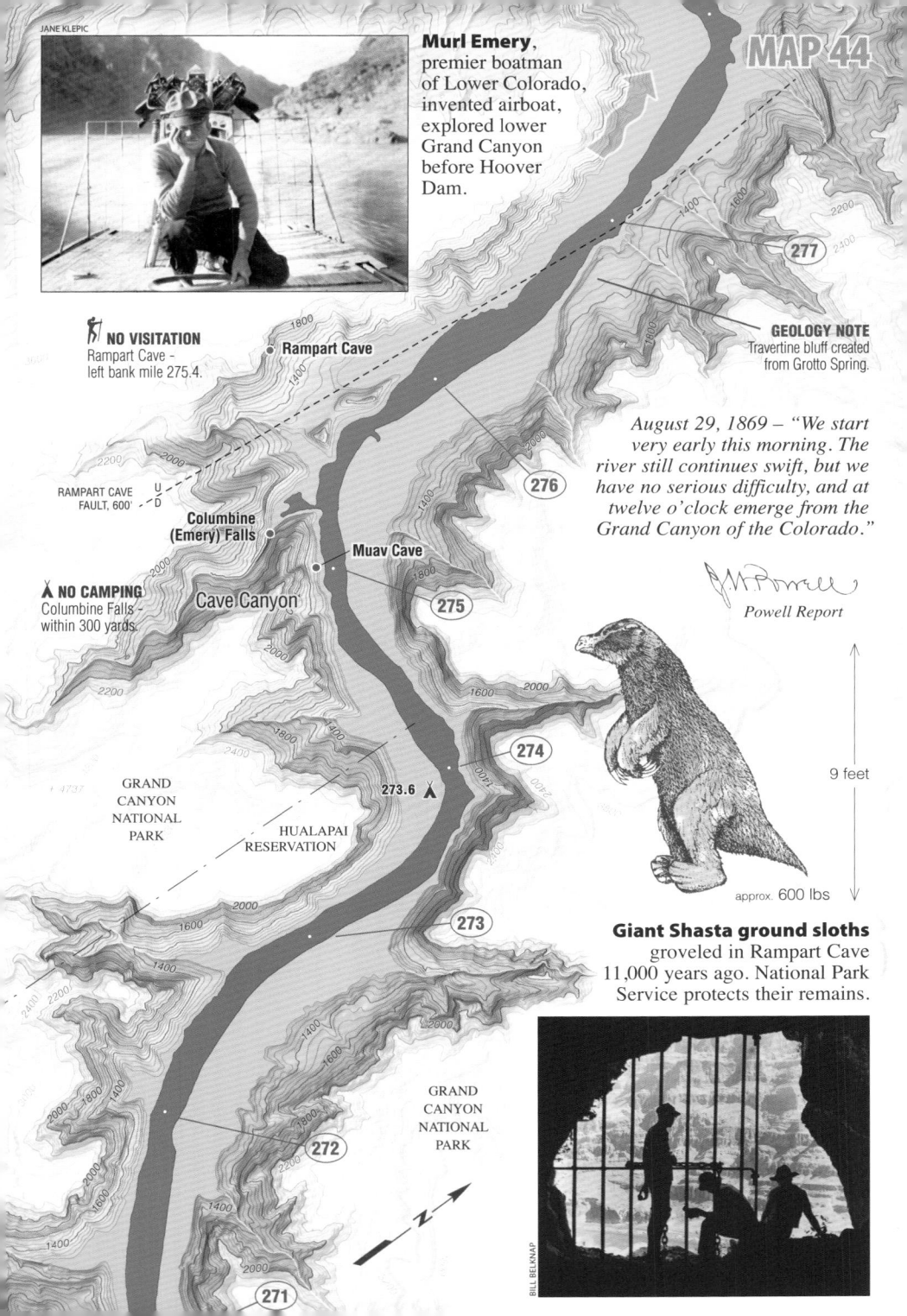

JANE KLEPIC

Murl Emery, premier boatman of Lower Colorado, invented airboat, explored lower Grand Canyon before Hoover Dam.

MAP 44

277

GEOLOGY NOTE
Travertine bluff created from Grotto Spring.

NO VISITATION
Rampart Cave - left bank mile 275.4.

● **Rampart Cave**

1800
1400

RAMPART CAVE FAULT, 600'
U
D

Columbine (Emery) Falls ●

Muav Cave

Cave Canyon

276

275

NO CAMPING
Columbine Falls - within 300 yards.

August 29, 1869 – "We start very early this morning. The river still continues swift, but we have no serious difficulty, and at twelve o'clock emerge from the Grand Canyon of the Colorado."

Powell Report

274

9 feet

approx. 600 lbs

GRAND CANYON NATIONAL PARK

HUALAPAI RESERVATION

273.6

273

Giant Shasta ground sloths groveled in Rampart Cave 11,000 years ago. National Park Service protects their remains.

GRAND CANYON NATIONAL PARK

272

271

BILL BELKNAP

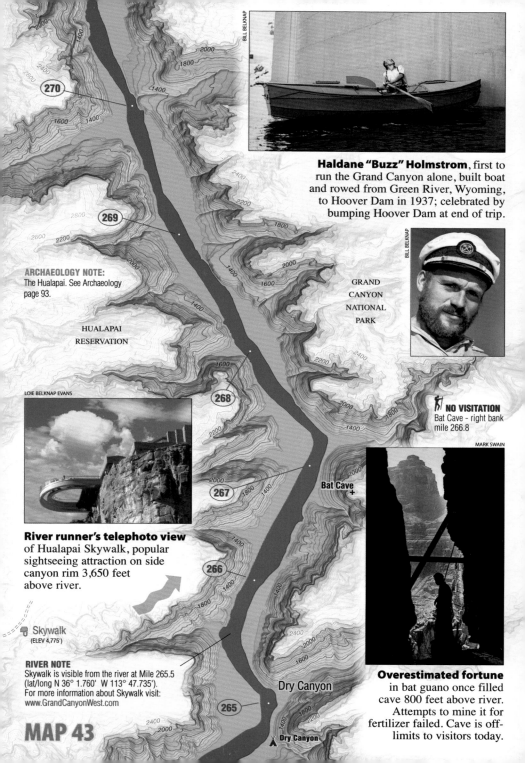

Haldane "Buzz" Holmstrom, first to run the Grand Canyon alone, built boat and rowed from Green River, Wyoming, to Hoover Dam in 1937; celebrated by bumping Hoover Dam at end of trip.

270

269

ARCHAEOLOGY NOTE:
The Hualapai. See Archaeology page 93.

HUALAPAI
RESERVATION

268

267

GRAND

CANYON

NATIONAL

PARK

NO VISITATION
Bat Cave - right bank mile 266.8

River runner's telephoto view
of Hualapai Skywalk, popular sightseeing attraction on side canyon rim 3,650 feet above river.

266

🚩 Skywalk
(ELEV 4,775')

RIVER NOTE
Skywalk is visible from the river at Mile 265.5 (lat/long N 36° 1.760' W 113° 47.735').
For more information about Skywalk visit:
www.GrandCanyonWest.com

Bat Cave
+

Dry Canyon

265

MAP 43

Dry Canyon

Overestimated fortune
in bat guano once filled cave 800 feet above river. Attempts to mine it for fertilizer failed. Cave is off-limits to visitors today.

MAP 46

Major Powell's chair lashed atop *Emma Dean*, 1872 trip.

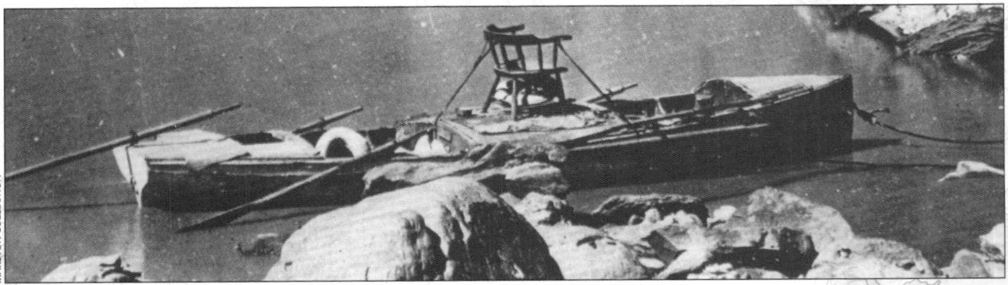
MARSTON COLLECTION

August 29, 1869–"The relief from danger and the joy of success are great. When he who has been chained by wounds to a hospital cot…at last goes out into the open field, what a world he sees! The first hour of convalescent freedom seems rich recompense for all pain and gloom and terror. Something like these are the feelings we experience tonight…The river rolls by us in silent majesty; the quiet of the camp is sweet; our joy is almost ecstasy."

J.W. Powell

Powell Report

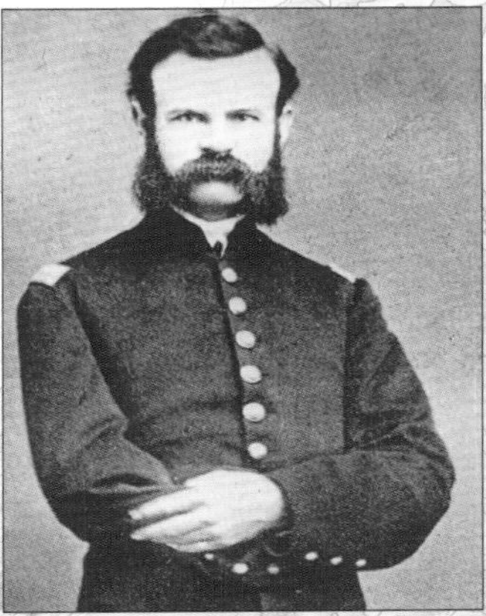
GEORGE COLLINS COLLECTION

Major Powell, about 1862.

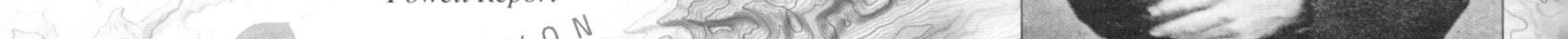
ICEBERG CANYON
2000
1800
1600
1400
Driftwood Cove
ICEBERG CANYON FAULT
D
U
NEVADA
ARIZONA
Chuckwalla Cove
1600
1400
Redwall Limestone
North Howland Cove
2000
1800
1400
Bradley Bay
Driftwood Island
Grand Wash Bay
1400
Twin Coves
WHEELER FAULT
D
U
1400
1600
Redwall Limestone
South America Point
Wheeler Ridge
2600
1600
1400
1800
God's Pocket
1800
1600
Badger Cove
1400

Pearce Ferry Rapid started as a small riffle in 2001. Now basically un-runnable, it flipped a 37-foot commercial pontoon boat in 2009. See additional information on page 25.

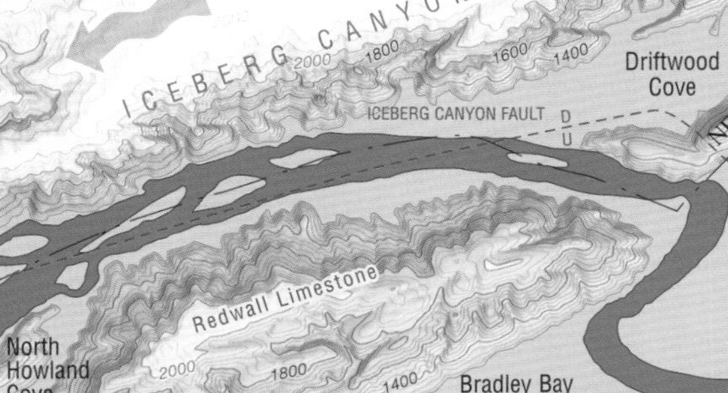
ARR
DAVID LOGAN

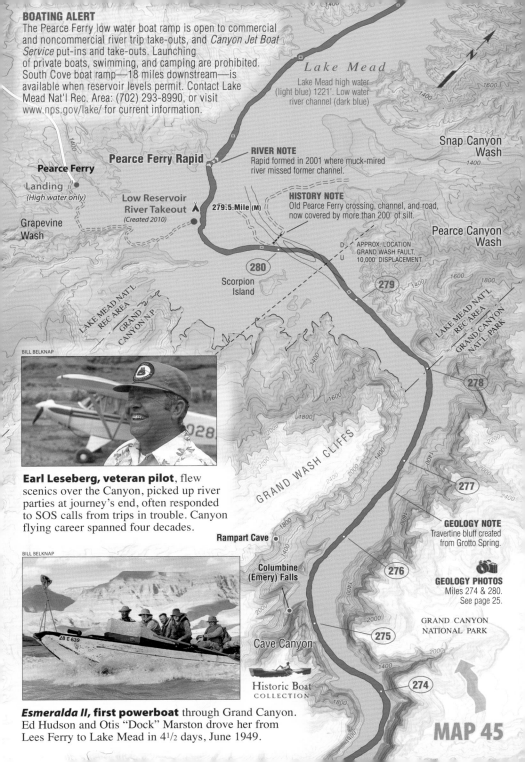

BOATING ALERT

The Pearce Ferry low water boat ramp is open to commercial and noncommercial river trip take-outs, and *Canyon Jet Boat Service* put-ins and take-outs. Launching of private boats, swimming, and camping are prohibited. South Cove boat ramp—18 miles downstream—is available when reservoir levels permit. Contact Lake Mead Nat'l Rec. Area: (702) 293-8990, or visit www.nps.gov/lake/ for current information.

Lake Mead
Lake Mead high water
(light blue) 1221'. Low water
river channel (dark blue)

Snap Canyon Wash

Pearce Ferry

Landing
(High water only)

Grapevine Wash

Pearce Ferry Rapid

RIVER NOTE
Rapid formed in 2001 where muck-mired
river missed former channel.

Low Reservoir River Takeout
(Created 2010)

279.5 Mile (M)

HISTORY NOTE
Old Pearce Ferry crossing, channel, and road,
now covered by more than 200' of silt.

Pearce Canyon Wash

APPROX. LOCATION
GRAND WASH FAULT,
10,000' DISPLACEMENT

280

Scorpion Island

279

LAKE MEAD NAT'L REC AREA
GRAND CANYON N.P.

LAKE MEAD NAT'L REC AREA
GRAND CANYON NAT'L PARK

278

BILL BELKNAP

Earl Leseberg, veteran pilot, flew scenics over the Canyon, picked up river parties at journey's end, often responded to SOS calls from trips in trouble. Canyon flying career spanned four decades.

GRAND WASH CLIFFS

277

Rampart Cave

GEOLOGY NOTE
Travertine bluff created
from Grotto Spring.

BILL BELKNAP

Columbine (Emery) Falls

GEOLOGY PHOTOS
Miles 274 & 280.
See page 25.

276

GRAND CANYON
NATIONAL PARK

275

Cave Canyon

Historic Boat
COLLECTION

274

***Esmeralda II,* first powerboat** through Grand Canyon. Ed Hudson and Otis "Dock" Marston drove her from Lees Ferry to Lake Mead in 4½ days, June 1949.

MAP 45

MAP 47

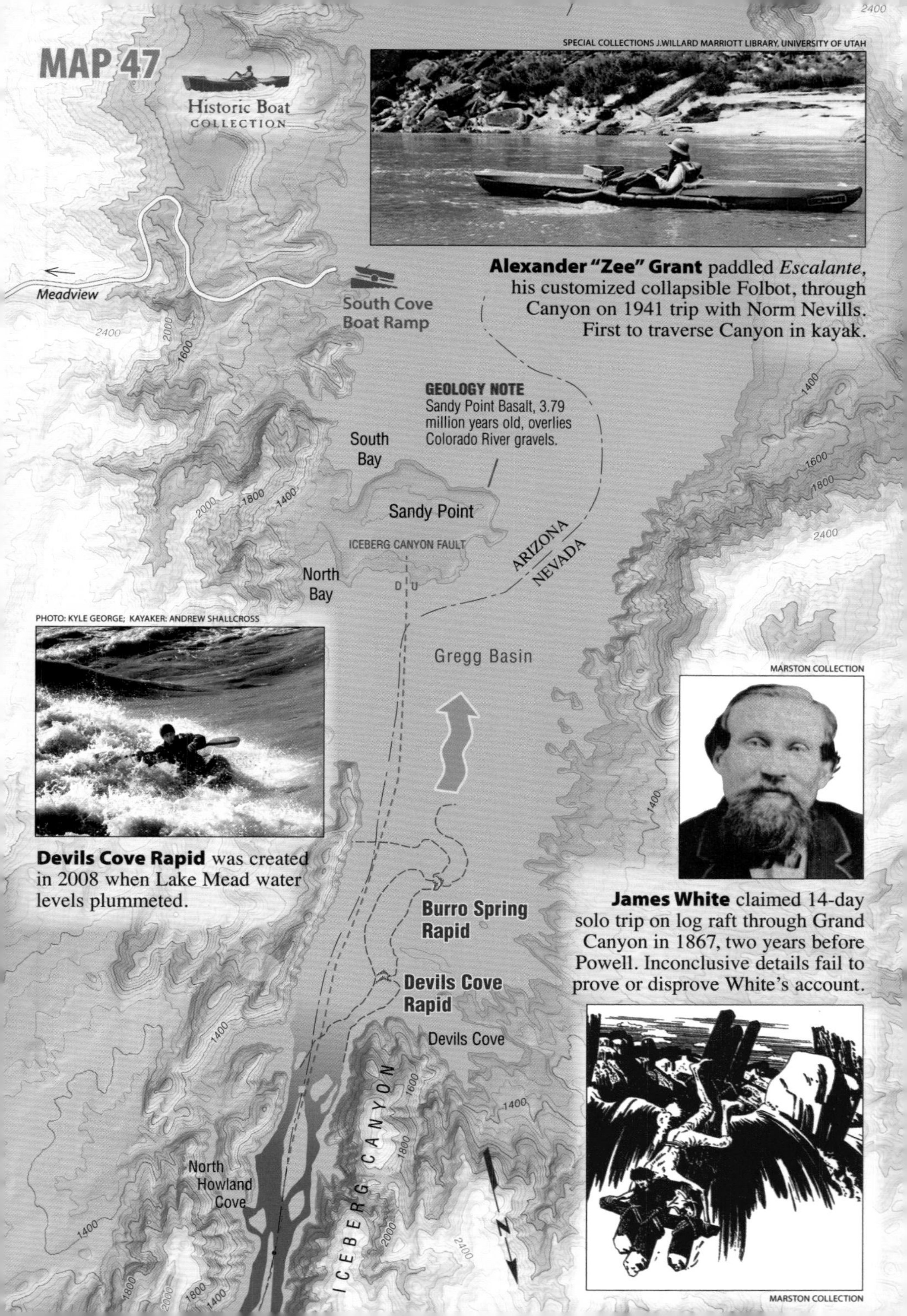

Historic Boat
COLLECTION
Meadview
South Cove
Boat Ramp
South
Bay
Sandy Point
ICEBERG CANYON FAULT
D U
North
Bay
ARIZONA
NEVADA
Gregg Basin
Burro Spring
Rapid
Devils Cove
Rapid
Devils Cove
ICEBERG CANYON
North
Howland
Cove
N
2400
2000
1600
1800
1400

GEOLOGY NOTE
Sandy Point Basalt, 3.79 million years old, overlies Colorado River gravels.

SPECIAL COLLECTIONS J.WILLARD MARRIOTT LIBRARY, UNIVERSITY OF UTAH

Alexander "Zee" Grant paddled *Escalante*, his customized collapsible Folbot, through Canyon on 1941 trip with Norm Nevills. First to traverse Canyon in kayak.

PHOTO: KYLE GEORGE; KAYAKER: ANDREW SHALLCROSS

Devils Cove Rapid was created in 2008 when Lake Mead water levels plummeted.

MARSTON COLLECTION

James White claimed 14-day solo trip on log raft through Grand Canyon in 1867, two years before Powell. Inconclusive details fail to prove or disprove White's account.

MARSTON COLLECTION

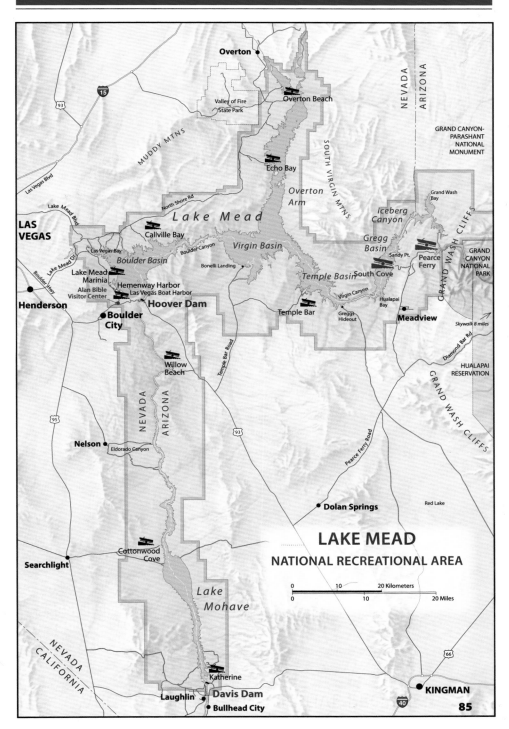

LAKE MEAD

LAKE MEAD
NATIONAL RECREATIONAL AREA

Overton
Valley of Fire State Park
Overton Beach
Echo Bay
Overton Arm
SOUTH VIRGIN MTNS
NEVADA
ARIZONA
GRAND CANYON-PARASHANT NATIONAL MONUMENT
MUDDY MTNS
North Shore Rd
Lake Mead
Callville Bay
Virgin Basin
Iceberg Canyon
Grand Wash Bay
Gregg Basin
GRAND WASH CLIFFS
LAS VEGAS
Las Vegas Blvd
Lake Mead Blvd
Las Vegas Bay
Boulder Canyon
Boulder Basin
Bonelli Landing
Sandy Pt.
Pearce Ferry
GRAND CANYON NATIONAL PARK
Lake Mead Dr
Lake Mead Marina
Temple Basin
South Cove
Henderson
Boulder Hwy
Alan Bible Visitor Center
Hemenway Harbor
Las Vegas Boat Harbor
Hoover Dam
Boulder City
Temple Bar
Virgin Canyon
Gregg's Hideout
Hualapai Bay
Meadview
Skywalk 8 miles
Diamond Bar Rd
HUALAPAI RESERVATION
Willow Beach
NEVADA
ARIZONA
Temple Bar Road
GRAND WASH CLIFFS
95
Nelson
Eldorado Canyon
93
Pearce Ferry Road
Dolan Springs
Red Lake
Cottonwood Cove
Lake Mohave
Searchlight
NEVADA
CALIFORNIA
Katherine
Laughlin
Davis Dam
Bullhead City
KINGMAN
66
40

0   10   20 Kilometers
0   10   20 Miles

85

BY DOUGLAS W. SCHWARTZ *(Updated by NPS Archaeologists: 2018)*

The first Grand Canyon Archaeologist

John Wesley Powell

Bright Angel Pueblo
as it might have looked
AD 1100-1140.

When John Wesley Powell floated the Grand Canyon in 1869, he recorded the first evidence that it had been occupied in prehistoric times by ancestral Native Americans. In Glen Canyon he had found ruins and speculated, correctly, that these were made centuries ago by ancestors of the Hopi, who currently live just to the east of the Grand Canyon. He was partly correct, too, in surmising that the people who had constructed these ruins came to "these cliffs and canyons" seeking protection from marauders. As the first archaeologist of the Grand Canyon, Powell also wrote that an old pueblo he discovered at Bright Angel Creek had been built by Indians fleeing invading Spaniards. He surmised, too, that other prehistoric people may have "inhabited this country anterior to the present Indian races."

Powell's observations about Grand Canyon prehistory were the beginning of modern Canyon archaeology, followed by numerous studies that have greatly expanded and modified his early conclusions. Today, for example, we have determined that the Bright Angel site is part of an ancestral pueblo settlement that predates the Spanish arrival by over 500 years. We also now know that all the prehistoric sites in the Canyon were built by the native peoples of the area who occupied the canyon's for at least the last 12,000 years.

Paleoindian Hunters

12,000- 3000 BC

For additional information, consult: *On the Edge of Splendor,* and *The Walhalla Plateau,* by Douglas W. Schwartz, available from SAR Press, www.sarweb.org/press/press.htm

Limited evidence exists for people referred to as Paleoindian in the Grand Canyon region at the end of the last ice age nearly 12,000 years ago. These people, thought to be following pathways through the glacial retreats to hunt big game such as the wooly mammoth, left scant evidence of their passing. At Grand Canyon, two distinctive projectile points, one known as "Clovis" and the other "Folsom" speak to some presence of these early hunters. The isolated nature of these finds gives us little indication of how early humans used the landscape other than the knowledge that they did pass through the Canyon. The environment would have been very different at the end of the ice age, with vegetation much different than we see today; it would have been a much wetter and colder place, at least for a little while. Once the climate started to stabilize, the high desert of the Colorado Plateau took hold and changed the environment again. No longer were the Pleistocene mammals wandering around the area and the hunters needed to adapt to the changing climate.

Archaic Hunters and imitative "magic"
3000-1000 BC

Split Twig Figurine

GRAND CANYON NATIONAL PARK
MUSEUM COLLECTION

Reference: *The Archaeology of Grand Canyon: Ancient Peoples, Ancient Places: Edited by Francis E. Smiley, Christian E. Downum, and Susan G. Smiley:* Grand Canyon Conservancy: 2018

Tools and weapons were chipped from chert, obsidian, and other hard stone.

GRAND CANYON NATIONAL PARK
MUSEUM COLLECTION

Specific evidence exists of ancestral people in the Grand Canyon at least five thousand years ago. Although evidence is limited, recent research along the Colorado River has shed some light on how these people were utilizing the resources of the canyon. We know that they hunted and gathered, made encampments, cooked foods and took advantage of seasonally available plants and animals in the Canyon's wide-ranging environments.

We do know about one type of their specialized paraphernalia—animal effigies made of split twigs probably representing bighorn sheep and stashed in caves above the river. Many of these figurines date from as early as 3000 BC.

Stanton's Cave, one of the figurine locations, can be seen at Mile 31.5. It is in the Redwall Limestone relatively close to the river. The way these figurines were made and their probable purpose provides a fascinating insight into one aspect of early Canyon life.

Some figurines are small enough to fit in the palm of your hand and were made following a precise pattern. Typically, a willow or cottonwood branch about the span of an arm was first split for most of its length; then the un-split portion was bent to become the back and back legs of the effigy. The two split ends of the branch were next bent to create the figurine's body, neck, head, and in some cases, horns.

At least two hundred of these animal shaped figurines (some appear to represent bighorn sheep, others deer) now have been found in twelve separate caves in and around the Grand Canyon. Their meticulous construction and placement suggests they were likely part of a ritual practiced by a hunting people who believed that magical forces tied the natural world together, and that by performing strictly prescribed rites, they could control these powerful forces and achieve a desired result. The split-twig figurine complex was not restricted to Grand Canyon. Similar figurines have been found in other portions of the southwest, primarily in

Pottery sherds
and other artifacts
provide an important
window into the
past. Archaeologists,
naturalists and the
National Park Service
prefer they be left as
found and not gathered
into collection piles
like those shown in the
photo above. Removing
artifacts is illegal.

Cultures in Transition
1000 BC - AD 1000

The Cohonina
AD 700-1200

the southern Great Basin and Green River areas, where the figurines have different construction methods and different placement patterns. All together, these early hunters made and placed these figurines for over 1700 years (85 generations), ranging in age from 2900 to 1250 B.C.

Anthropologists refer to this practice as imitative magic because it mimics a wished-for outcome. Since the protein-rich bighorn sheep roaming the inner Canyon were always vigilant and difficult to approach, hunters prepared with great care, buttressing their skill and luck with a traditional magic ritual in which the figurines may have played an important role.

During the next two thousand years native people living in the Canyon region continued their hunting and gathering life. Some remaining artifacts—buried hearths, roasting pits, occasional finds of basketry, and later, scatterings of pottery—suggest that the Canyon was being used throughout this time.

While few sites with pottery or domesticated plant remains have been excavated that date prior to AD 1000, there is evidence that some corn, beans, and probably squash were being grown before this time while hunting and gathering were still being practiced.

Finally, about AD 700, the transition to farming and a more settled life is evident with the coming of the Cohonina, a Hopi word meaning "the people who live to the west."

Initially, the Cohonina lived in brush structures and moved seasonally like earlier foragers, gathering wild plants and hunting rabbits, deer, rats, squirrels, prairie dogs, antelope, and birds. Gradually, over the next four to five hundred years, they built more substantial buildings and constructed low stone dams across dry washes, possibly to catch rain runoff for farming.

Cohonina settlements were first located on the plateau south of the Grand Canyon. About AD 900 their numbers began to increase dramatically, probably because of better weather brought on by a warm and wet period in many parts of the world. For the next hundred years or so their population expanded. For a short time around AD 900 they even spread north of the river to Unkar Delta (Mile 72.5), where they experimented with farming.

The Cohonina had tools for hunting, gathering (heavily relying on pinyon nuts on the plateau), and presumably farming, including grinding stones and stone mortars, as well as distinctively shaped points for arrows and spearheads; stone drills for woodworking; and scrapers and blades for preparing skins. They made a distinctive pottery, called San Francisco Mountain Gray Ware, and rock art attributed to them has been found at springs and permanent water holes.

Around AD 1150 a major drop in precipitation and temperature, corresponding with the onset of a period of worldwide cooling known as the Little Ice Age, spread over the whole northern Colorado Plateau and caused a serious decline in the Cohonina population. By about AD 1200 all settlements identifiable as Cohonina were gone. Recent work in the Coconino basin suggests that the Cohonina population centers moved farther to the east, before being subsumed within other cultural traditions.

Metate, or grinding stone for corn, and mano, a hand stone used with it.

The Puebloans
AD 800-1200

About AD 800, a century after the Cohonina appeared in the western Grand Canyon region, pueblo people moved in from the east. These pueblo people were ancestral to the Hopi, who still live just east of the Canyon and the Little Colorado River. Other modern day Puebloan groups, most notably the Zuni, also view the ancestral Puebloans of the Canyon as their ancestors.

Pueblo people began to regularly use the Canyon region before AD 1000, perhaps hunting, gathering and farming. Over the next two centuries, beginning about AD 1000, as the climate improved, the pueblo population rapidly increased, and dwellings were built in nearly every farmable area within the Canyon, and on the North and South rims. The only exception was the territory to the southwest used by the Cohonina.

Around AD 1050 pueblo people were living in small pit house and stone dwellings, with above ground

BILL BELKNAP

Hilltop Ruins above Unkar Delta
(see River Map Mile 72.5)

Nankoweap Granary

(see River Map 10 - mile 52.5)

ADAPTED FROM GRAND CANYON
NATIONAL PARK MUSEUM COLLECTION
PHOTO

Puebloan seed jar
dates from
AD 1000-1150

GRAND CANYON NATIONAL PARK
MUSEUM COLLECTION

shades or awnings made of brush and supported by cottonwood poles. They planted corn, beans, cotton and squash, and continued to hunt and gather. But, within a quarter of a century, they were living in well-planned, above-ground pueblos consisting of several rooms, and for the first time they built subterranean, ceremonial kivas within the inner Canyon.

Eventually, the pueblo people constructed hundreds of living sites containing single-to-many room dwellings, religious structures, rock-terraced agricultural fields, cliff granaries, rock-lined roasting pits, petroglyphs, and pictographs.

More than one thousand of these living sites have been found in the Canyon region, including pueblos my team and I excavated on Unkar Delta, at the mouth of Bright Angel Creek, and on the North Rim's Walhalla Plateau.

These ruins can be seen along an archaeological trail the National Park Service has built on Unkar Delta. The Delta was heavily settled after AD 1100, as were side canyons like Nankoweap (Mile 52.5) and Shinumo (Mile 109) and Tapeats (Mile 134.4).

One striking reminder of the Nankoweap occupation is a beautifully constructed stone granary built high on the north cliff wall immediately downstream from the entry of Nankoweap Canyon into the Colorado River.

Many river runners climb to Nankoweap granary, on a well-used trail, to examine this vivid illustration of the lengths to which the early pueblo people went to protect their food in the harsh environment.

Further downstream, at the mouth of Bright Angel Creek (Mile 88), just above the bank of the Colorado River, lies the small pueblo discovered by Powell. This dwelling included several living rooms with hearths, separate storage rooms, and partially walled roofed work areas. In a plaza facing the rooms was a subterranean kiva. This site also can be easily visited, just off the Bright Angel Trail beyond the river bridge.

Pueblo people also spread to the North Rim where they built dwellings and agricultural storage facilities at Walhalla. Today, Walhalla Glades ruin is reached from

the Cape Royal Road. They may have planted within the Canyon in the early spring, and moved to the higher, cooler, rainier North Rim to farm during its short summer season.

By the mid-twelfth century climatic changes related to the Little Ice Age made farming in the Canyon region increasingly difficult. The North Rim settlements tapered off, and recent evidence from NPS excavations along the river suggest that the residents along the river remained for another generation, through approximately 1250 A.D., before migrating to areas outside the Canyon.

One of the last Puebloan settlements in the Canyon region is located on the South Rim a few miles east of the present Grand Canyon Village. Tusayan Pueblo was constructed late in the occupation of the Canyon region, between AD 1190 and 1209. It consists of eight well-made, single story rooms, built around a U-shaped plaza and includes two ceremonial kivas. By about AD 1225 or slightly later, it too, was abandoned. A visit to Tusayan Ruin and Museum will provide a glimpse of Pueblo Indian life at Grand Canyon some 800 years ago. A self-guiding trail leads through the adjacent ruin. Ranger-led tours are offered daily. Educational materials about the Park and region are sold in the non-profit bookstore.

Where did they go?

Why did both the Cohonina and Puebloan occupation of the Canyon end at the same time, around the beginning of the thirteenth century? The disappearance of Cohonina and Puebloan peoples may have been one effect of a major change in the climate over the whole northern hemisphere during that period. The long mild and moist centuries of the earlier period which fostered the increase in human populations in the Grand Canyon region and throughout the Southwest came to an end about AD 1200 with the onset of the Little Ice Age, when temperatures in the North Atlantic began dropping and the Atlantic ice pack increased.

The story of human use and occupation of the Canyons is one of exploration and movement, of cultural traditions and adaptations. What began as loosely connected hamlets gradually developed into multi-generational homesteads throughout much of the Canyon, and certainly along the Colorado River. Cultural constructs, including migration histories, may have played a role in the eventual decline and movement from the Canyon to more favorable locations to the east, like the Hopi Mesas.

The Hopi

Hisatsinom (Puebloan) descendents

Hopi Niman Kachinas

FROM 1945 PAINTING BY HOPI ARTIST FRED KABOTIE

Contact:
Hopi - Kykotsmovi, AZ
www.hopi-nsn.gov

The Hopi, who consider themselves descendents of the Hisatsinom (a Hopi word meaning people of long ago), live on mesas seventy miles east of the Canyon today. They believe that the Grand Canyon was a place their ancestors journeyed through and left "footprints at stopping places along the way"— sites where they were given the knowledge of rituals that eventually allowed them to reside at their final home on the Hopi Mesas. Sipapuni, the navel from which they believe their ancestors emerged from a previous world, is a travertine dome of rock in the Little Colorado River section of the Grand Canyon. Sipapuni, a revered Hopi sacred site, is off limits to visitors. It is here and to nearby salt-bearing ledges that generations of Hopi males have returned to complete their transition to manhood.

The Hopi also believe that the spirits of some Hopi clan members return to the Grand Canyon after death, traveling through the sipapuni to the underworld, and then on to their next life. From there they may return to the land of the living Hopi as "...billowy clouds...to drop rain upon our parched land."

Early Paiute and Ancestral Hualapai and Havasupai

AD 800-1200

The Grand Canyon probably was used only occasionally during most of the thirteenth century. Then, sometime between AD 1200 to 1300, from the north and west came a new hunting and gathering people, the Paiute; also, at this time, a foraging people, ancestors of the Hualapai and Havasupai, came from the west and south.

Major John Wesley Powell with Tau-ruv, a member of the Paiute Indian Tribe in the Uinta Valley,1870s.

Contact:
Southern Paiute
Consortium,
Fredonia, AZ
www.kaibabpaiute-nsn.gov/
SPC.html

O n August 26, 1869, John Wesley Powell and his hungry crew came across a garden along the bank of the river in the western part of the Canyon. Helping themselves to "…ten or a dozen…nice green squashes," they sped a short distance downriver to a safer site where they dined on squash, unleavened bread, and coffee. "Never was fruit so sweet as these stolen squashes,…" Powell later wrote.

The Paiute, who probably cultivated the garden that Powell and his men discovered, lived north of and within the Grand Canyon. Known as the Kaibab band, they belonged then and now to a larger group of Southern Paiutes who speak a Uto-Aztecan language and have a deep ancestry reaching thousands of years into the past.

The prehistoric Southern Paiute way of life is poorly known, but elders have suggested to anthropologists that their ancestors lived in small related groups comprised of parents, unmarried children, and a few grandparents. They dressed in simple buckskins, dwelt in houses of stacked pine boughs, and kept a minimum of utensils. The seasonal searches for food sources kept them on the move hunting for game on the high plateaus in the fall, moving into the Canyon when it became colder. Their most important winter food may have come from agave plants which in winter store up sugars in their root stalks, the hearts of which were collected and roasted. In the early spring, when food was most difficult to find, they depended on juniper berries and other marginal foods. In late spring, they collected quail and grouse eggs and began to hunt.

The Southern Paiute believe that all of nature— boulders, water seeps, vegetation, mammals, birds, and even insects—have a life-essence for which the people have a reverential appreciation. All nature, and especially springs, are occupied by spirits to which the Paiute sacrifice with suitable offerings. The Southern Paiute people, like other indigenous people of the area, have been living in the Canyon since time immemorial.

The Hualapai

Hualapai enterprises include cattle ranching, timber sales, arts and crafts, and other tourist adventures.

T he Hualapai, literally "people of the tall pines," together with their cultural and linguistic cousins, the Havasupai, expanded into the region south of the Colorado River sometime after AD 1200. Some thirteen hundred Hualapai now live on a reservation of a million and a half acres bordered on the north by 108 miles of the Colorado River and the Grand Canyon and extending some fifty miles south to the Bill Williams Mountains.

Contact:
Hualapai
Peach Springs, AZ
www.grandcanyonwest.
com

The early Hualapai traditionally moved seasonally between the plateau and the Canyon, hunting and gathering in different environmental zones as food became seasonally available. They hunted deer, antelope, and mountain lion for food, fur, and hides. They gathered cactus fruit, grass seeds, and other wild plants, and, after the end of the Little Ice Age, also planted corn, beans and squash, both on the plateau and in the Canyon where there were springs to water their gardens. They built small brush and bark dome houses in each new camp they moved to throughout the year.

The Havasupai

For reservations and hiking permits contact:
Contact: 928-448-2121
www.havasupai-nsn.gov

The Havasupai, "people of the blue-green water," are the only indigenous people still living within the Grand Canyon. They reside in a side canyon, south of the Colorado River (Mile 158), a narrow oasis of green fields, red cliffs, and exceptionally beautiful waterfalls. Along with their close relatives, the Hualapai, the Havasupai believe they came into existence at a place called Spirit Mountain to the west of the Grand Canyon.

Historically, the Havasupai farmed within their canyon home during the warmer months, using the ample water of Havasu Creek to irrigate their fields of corn, beans, and squash. After their August harvest they moved to the higher plateau south of the Canyon where they hunted and gathered, using practices similar to those of the Paiute who lived to the north, and probably like the foragers who had occupied the land thousands of years before. Together with the other peoples of the time they depended upon hunting pronghorn antelope, mule deer, bobcats, rabbits, turkeys, and porcupine, as well as gathering the seasonal plant foods from within the Canyon and over the plateaus. The Havasupai also traded buckskin and basketry to the Hualapai and Hopi.

BILL BELKNAP

Supai Village

Today, many Havasupai Indians try to live by the traditional concept of harmony with all life. They want to preserve the natural beauty of their homeland and see themselves as being an inseparable part of the land. They believe that if their homeland is destroyed so are they.

Zuni

Pueblo of Zuni -
Zuni, NM

------->

From the book:
Zuni and the Courts,
edited by
Richard Hart 1995.

The Navajo

The Navajo Nation
Window Rock, AZ

------->

Quote from the book:
*We Call the Canyon
Home:* Navajo chapter:
Richard Begay
Publisher: Grand
Canyon Conservancy

**Native
American Tribes**
with ancestral roots in
Grand Canyon are active
in the monitoring and
preservation of cultural
resources through the Glen
Canyon Dam Adaptive
Management program:

- **Navajo (Dine')**
- **Hopi Tribe**
- **Havasupai**
- **Hualapai Tribe**
- **Zuni**
- **Yavapai-Apache**
- **Kaibab Paiute**
- **Paiute Tribe of Utah**
- **Las Vegas Paiute**
- **Moapa Paiute**
- **San Juan Southern Paiute**

A ccording to Zuni historians, the Zuni people emerged onto this world at a place within Grand Canyon called Chimik'yana'kya dey'a, near Ribbon Falls in Bright Angel Canyon within Grand Canyon National Park. The natural environment that Zuni people saw at Emergence became central to traditional Zuni culture. All of the plants that grow along the stream from Ribbon Falls to the Colorado River, and all the birds and other animals, springs, minerals, and natural resources located in the Grand Canyon and its tributaries have a central place in Zuni traditional cultural practices and ceremonial activities. (Hart)

T he Navajo, do not believe they originated in the Grand Canyon, but do believe that its rugged topography forms the protective western boundary of their people. Offerings and prayers are made to the Canyon, and water from the Colorado River is used during Navajo ceremonies.

"The Navajo people have a rich history with the Grand Canyon, including the various names people use for the Grand Canyon including Tsé Chíí' Koo' (Red Wall Canyon), Tsékooh Hatsaa' (Big Rock Canyon), and a very descriptive work for Grand Canyon Village, Bidáá' Ha'azt'i' (Railroad Coming to the Edge).

The canyons that make up the Grand Canyon system helped to shape the Navajo people. The canyons know the Navajo people, who have lived here since time immemorial. The canyons created the beauty of the Navajo lifeway; Navajo people honor that creation in traditions, language, kinship, history, and ceremonies. Much like their ancestors, the Navajo people access the resources in the canyons to maintain their daily lives, to pass on their cultural traditions and knowledge, and to celebrate who they are."

T he prehistory of the Grand Canyon region will never be completely understood; many intriguing questions are yet to be answered about how ancestral peoples lived here and how their ways of life evolved. John Wesley Powell promoted ethnographic, archaeological, and linguistic research throughout his life, and, like the Native Americans he met, viewed people and their environment as intrinsically interconnected. Like Powell, the archaeologists, anthropologists, and naturalists of today continue to use the latest techniques to discover, excavate, interpret, and preserve new sites in order to reveal more about the early people who struggled to survive in the vast and varied Grand Canyon.

BY MERIBETH M. RIFFEY WITH JODI PARRY BELKNAP

LOIE BELKNAP EVANS

Monarch butterfly pollinates Rocky Mountain Bee plant blossom as it moves among plants, feeding on their sweet nectar.

SMITHSONIAN INSTITUTION PHOTO

Clinton Hart Merriam studied plants and wildlife in the Grand Canyon, developed theory of life zones.

A Pictorial Guide to Plants and Animals begins on page 104.

The Grand Canyon teems with life. Its many climatic environments support an extraordinary diversity of animals and plants. Their habitats range from the freezing, snow-wrapped winters of the high Kaibab Plateau to the parched summers of the central Inner Gorge where ground-level temperatures sometimes exceed 125 degrees F.

Clinton Hart Merriam, who helped found the National Geographic Society and what is now the U.S. Fish and Wildlife Service, made the first official biological study of the Canyon in 1889. Merriam divided the Canyon into elevation belts, called life zones, that support different types of plants and animals. Although today's naturalists use the term community to more accurately categorize groups of interdependent plants and animals, the zone designations set by Merriam still are helpful to visitors who want to know where to look for certain flowers, trees, mammals, birds, and other wildlife.

Two life zones are found along the Colorado River: the Upper Sonoran Zone, an area of desert scrub and piñon-juniper, and the Lower Sonoran Zone, a desert area.

Within these zones two biologic communities can be identified readily by river travelers: the desert scrub community, and the wetland riverbank community naturalists call riparian. Plants and animals making their homes in these regions thrive in spite of a climate marked by intense heat and flash floods in summer, extremes of temperature in winter, and year-round aridity. They exhibit some remarkable adaptations that allow them to make the best use of available resources.

Plants. The flowers, shrubs, trees, and cacti visible to river travelers add fascinating shapes and colors to the landscape. Habitat-bound plants overcome challenges of the harsh environment with techniques such as shedding leaves, putting down long roots, storing water in expandable stems, and emitting substances toxic to other plants.

Flowers. More than 1,750 different flowering plants have been identified in the Canyon. Desert flowers have an extraordinary ability to remain dormant during long periods of drought, then burst into bloom when winter rains have been plentiful, bringing pockets of painted

Biologic Community
A group of plants and animals living together and dependent on each other through food chains and other interrelationships; for example, the riparian community bordering the Colorado River.

Habitat
The local environment of a plant or animal including everything necessary for its existence.

Niche
The role played by a particular organism in the community; for instance, the turkey vulture's *niche* is that of a scavenger.

For additional information, consult:
River and Desert Plants of the Grand Canyon by Kristin Huisinga, Lori Makarick and Kate Watters, Mountain Press Publishing Co., 2006.

beauty to dull-colored side canyons and gray, boulder-strewn washes. Those who miss this seasonal sight can take comfort in knowing that flowers bloom year-round in the wet seeps and springs of Vasey's Paradise, Elves Chasm, Havasu Canyon, and other water-rich sites along the river which support equally striking flowering perennials for much of the rest of the year. Watch for a yellow flash of blooming prince's plume framed against a blue sky, a crimson cardinal monkeyflower seen brightening a sidestream oasis, or a night-blooming sand-verbena as it fills a campsite with fragrance from its tiny white blossoms.

Shrubs and Trees. Ocotillo is the spindly, flame-tipped plant frequently seen reaching skyward from craggy outcroppings after about Mile 153.5 on the river. To conserve life-giving moisture, it sheds the tiny leaves on its spines when the Canyon becomes too arid.

Mesquite and its look-alike, the catclaw acacia, seen on higher ground and in side canyons, fold in their dainty olive-green leaves to reduce exposure to the sun and retain moisture. Both have the added advantage of a deep-

Ocotillo *-Fouquieria splendens*

reaching root system which can penetrate the ground more than 50 feet in order to tap into water.

Many common shrubs found along the river corridor help to stabilize the soil with their spreading root systems, including several species of *baccharis*. One hardy long-time resident species which thrives on riverbank flooding is the coyote willow, the plant used by ancestral Native American hunters in the Canyon to make split twig figurines.

The evergreen creosote bush is thought to emit a root toxin that deters other plants from sharing its water supply. A waxy coating allows its leaves to retain moisture, making it one of the most drought-tolerant

NATIONAL PARK SERVICE - LORI MAKARICK

Tamarisk
Tamarix ramosissima

NATIONAL PARK SERVICE - PETER WILLIAMS

Tamarisk Beetle
Diorhabda carinulata

Exotic or non-native species have traveled beyond their traditional ranges and begun to invade foreign landscapes. If able to adapt quickly and spread rapidly to new environments they are called **invasive**, often posing a threat to native species.

plants in North America. It has a reputation as a nurse plant, providing protection for other plants and playing host to many insects whose survival depends on feasting on the plant's tiny yellow flowers.

Tamarisk, an exotic tree imported from Eurasia in the 1800s, had reached the Canyon by the 1930s. After the completion of Glen Canyon Dam in 1963, its distribution expanded. Because of its threat to native ecosystems, tamarisk, along with a handful of plant species listed in the box below, was targeted for control by the National Park Service. Since 2002 the NPS, its staff, partners and volunteers have removed more than 290,000 tamarisk trees from side canyons. The program is labor intensive and expensive, so removal from the main river corridor seemed implausible until recently.

NATIONAL PARK SERVICE - MELISSA MCMASTER

Tamarisk Beetle's larva and adult stages feed only on tamarisk, causing conspicuous defoliation and visible browning.

Now, the northern tamarisk beetle *(Diorhabda carinulata)*, a biological control agent imported into the U.S., may have changed the situation. First released upstream in Utah, the beetle reached the Grand Canyon by 2009. Since their arrival, tamarisk beetles have continued to spread throughout the river corridor and can be observed from April through September. Both larvae and adults feed on tamarisk, causing defoliation and stress, and ultimately weakening the tree enough to die. National Park Service biologists are hopeful that native species will expand into former tamarisk patches, but park staff and partners including the river community initiated active riparian restoration with a pilot project at Granite Camp in 2012. Dead tree removal, native species planting, and site restoration will occur at 2–3 additional sites over the next few years.

LEAST WANTED

Tamarisk *-Tamarix ramosissima*
Ravenna Grass *-Saccharum ravennae*
Camelthorn *-Alhagi maurorum*
Perennial Pepperweed *-Lepidium latifolium*
Russian Thistle *-Salsola tragus*
Russian Olive *-Elaeagnus angustifolia*
Sahara Mustard *-Brassica tournefortii*
Sowthistles *-Sonchus spp.*
Siberian Elm *-Ulmus pumila*

Southwestern Willow Flycatcher
-Empidonax traillii.
Riparian habitat created by Glen Canyon Dam has helped this endangered species to persist. Ironically the invasive tamarisk is one of its favorite nesting spots.

Wetland Riverbank Community

Where:
Along the edges of streams and riverbanks, in constantly moist soil.

Who and What:
Known to biologists as the riparian community, this is often an area of thick vegetation, amphibians, birds, and water-dwelling mammals. Residents include cottonwood, willow, mesquite, tamarisk, ringtail cat, spotted skunk, mule deer, dipper, mallard, stilt, common yellowthroat, whipsnake, Woodhouse's toad, and beaver.

Cacti. Cacti seen in the Canyon store moisture in unusually shaped stems that swell and shrink as water is absorbed. Prickly-pear and beavertail cacti store water in oval, pad-like stems that become wrinkled during drought periods. The barrel cactus stores moisture in a single barrel-shaped stem that expands and contracts according to the season.

The teddy-bear cholla—less huggable than its shape and name imply—has a dense, downy-looking covering of light-colored spines. Like the white or tan clothing worn by river runners who've planned ahead well, the spines reflect the sun, helping the cholla to stay cooler.

The ugly duckling appearance of many varieties of cacti is offset by the showy surprise of their spring and summer blossoms. Perched amid prickly spines, in hues of yellow, red, pink, and purple, the colorful blossoms delight the eye.

Animals. Inbred adaptations and the advantage of mobility help more than 450 different kinds of reptiles, amphibians, birds, and mammals meet the challenge of survival in the harsh Canyon environment.

Reptiles. Lizards and snakes have lived in the Canyon long enough to develop some elaborate survival tools. Variations in coloring protect them to some extent from their many predators, including each other. Since their body heat is regulated by environment, few reptiles can remain in the sun for long, although some desert lizards are able to pant to cool themselves. As water evaporates from their lungs, body temperature drops.

Desert lizards, which have higher temperature tolerances than snakes, are largely diurnal. Competition for moisture is so keen that most are carnivores, eating food that has at least a sixty percent water content.

Snakes most often sighted include the Grand Canyon rattlesnake and the California king snake. A constrictor, the king snake counts the Grand Canyon rattler among its prey. Snakes, which hibernate during the winter, are active from April through fall in the Canyon, often becoming nocturnal during hot weather.

Amphibians. Of the few amphibians living along the river, the red-spotted toad and Canyon treefrog are the most frequently seen. An ability to absorb moisture through their skins helps them survive. The loud voice of the male Canyon treefrog is thought by some biologists to be an adaptation that brings males and females together quickly when there is enough water in which to breed.

NATURAL HISTORY

California Condor
-Gymnogyps californianus.
Welcome Home.

Desert Scrub Community

Where:
On the Tonto Plateau and Esplanade, and in the Inner Gorge removed from the Colorado River, primarily below 4,500 feet in altitude.

Who and What:
Prevalent residents are blackbrush and other drought-resistant plants such as the Utah agave, yucca, ocotillo, beavertail, and hedgehog cacti. Animals include bighorn sheep, kangaroo rat, ringtail cat, canyon wren, Grand Canyon rattlesnake, collared lizard, and chuckwalla.

Birds. Some three hundred species of birds have been observed in the Canyon. About forty are year-round residents. In summer birds can escape the heat by flying to pools and streams for baths or by riding thermals to higher altitudes. Their normal body temperature of 104-106 degrees F. also makes it easier for them to tolerate high desert temperatures. Like many mammals, birds pant when they are overheated.

Water birds and shorebirds love the wetlands of the river and are seen fishing in shallows, eddies, and side-stream backwaters. Look for avocets, grebes, mallards, stilts, herons, and others. The eye-catching sight of a great blue heron soaring overhead on its six-foot wingspread is likely to stir a primordial response in anyone who can imagine an older, different Canyon not quite so changed by time and the river.

Birds of prey to watch for on cliffs and treetops include the golden and bald eagles, red-tailed hawk, and peregrine falcon; scavengers often seen are the common raven and turkey vulture. The Canyon has its share of songbirds. Many are new arrivals, attracted to woodland nesting sites established since control over seasonal flooding was made possible by the building of Glen Canyon Dam in 1963. Listen for the hooded oriole, Lucy's warbler, canyon wren, and others during early morning hours.

The California condor is returning to the Canyon after near extinction. In the early 1990s a conservation group in California, the Peregrine Fund, began rebuilding the population through a captive propagation program. The goal was to eventually establish a self-sustaining population that would allow the condor to be removed from the federal endangered species list. In 1996 the first condors were released in Grand Canyon. Reproduction

Canyon Wren
Catherpes Mexicanus.
Heard but seldom seen, the canyon wren's distinctive descending notes fill the immensity of the Canyon. Rust-colored with contrasting white throat. Likes rocky slopes near water. Uses long bill to probe crevices for spiders and insects.

Merriam's Kangaroo Rat-*Dipodomys merriami.* Buff-colored, four-toed, long-tailed rodent highly adapted for desert survival. Needs little water. Specialized kidneys four times more efficient than man's. Converts mesquite and ocotillo seeds, grass, into water. Bipedal. Hops like a kangaroo on long legs, using tail for balance. Deep burrows shelter it from heat.

in the wild was achieved in 2003 when the first condor chick was born. Currently, there are 73 reported to be flying free in northern Arizona, including some that were raised in wild nest caves in or around the Grand Canyon. More info at www.nps.gov/grca

Mammals. Mammals deal with the problems of water scarcity and Canyon heat in several ways. Large mammals such as bighorn sheep come down to the river to drink and browse when their usual cliffside abodes become too parched.

Smaller mammals unable to travel far in search of water get the liquid they need from food. The kangaroo rat, for example, may live its entire life without taking a single drink of water.

Many mammals retire to caves and nests to escape the midday heat and rest prior to the night's hunting. Coyotes, for instance, seek out the shade of a natural cave or protected crevice. Rodents, such as the rock pocket mouse, snuggle into burrows where the soil temperature is several degrees cooler than on the desert surface. Rabbits dig a shallow depression called a form, conveniently placed in the shade of a shrub. Beavers avoid heat and aridity by making the cool water of the river their principal habitat.

More than a twenty different species of bats found in the Canyon escape the heat altogether by inhabiting cool caves and dark, overhanging rock recesses during the day. Harmless to man, the insect-loving creatures emerge in droves at night to flit speedily about campsites, searching for flying edibles attracted to the glimmer of lanterns and flashlights.

The best time to look for mammals along the river is at dawn or dusk when those with both daytime and nighttime patterns are out and about. Burrows, dens, or nests are usually located near water sources. Look for paw or hoof prints next to side canyon springs and in muddy areas near the river. Then find a concealed spot downwind of a likely site and wait quietly.

A river trip provides a rare opportunity to be a guest in a living plant and wildlife community. Observant river travelers will leave the Canyon with a deepened awareness and respect for nature's incredible ways.

GLENN AND MARTHA VARGAS © CALIFORNIA ACADEMY OF SCIENCES

MAMMALS   *by Loie Belknap Evans*

NATIONAL PARK SERVICE - MARK LELLOUCH

Desert Bighorn - *Ovis canadensis.* Canyon country
native seen more frequently now that their major food
competitors, wild burros, have been removed from the
Canyon by the National Park Service.

Coyote - *Canis latrans.* Highly
adaptable, opportunistic, omnivorous
feeder. Wide-ranging in North America,
inhabits higher reaches of Canyon
country. Known for plaintive cry heard
in early evening, morning.

ALLEN GILBERG

Mule Deer - *Odocoileus hemionus.* Mule
deer feed, drink, find shade in riparian
vegetation of Canyon.

CHARLY HEAVENRICH

Ringtail Cat - *Bassariscus astutus.*
Nocturnal camp raider and raccoon cousin
often lives in rock crevices near river. Long,
distinctively marked tail offers balance
for negotiating narrow ledges, precarious
spaces. Agile, clever climber eats berries,
prickly pear fruit, stolen camp fare.

Beaver -*Castor canadensis*. Large rodent once hunted nearly to extinction is seen year-round in Canyon. Builds burrows and dens into riverbanks. Feeds on riparian vegetation. Uses paddle-shaped tail as rudder. Ears and nostrils can be sealed when submerged.

Spotted Skunk -*Spilogale gracilis*. Decidedly un-cuddly skunk often seen in Canyon. Nocturnal, omnivorous. Eats rodents, birds, eggs, vegetable matter. Nests in burrows, rock piles.

NATIONAL PARK SERVICE

CELIA SOUTHWICK

White-tailed Antelope Squirrel
Ammospermophilus leucurus. Small squirrel keeps cool by carrying tail over its back, reflecting heat with white underside.

Bushy-tailed Woodrat -*Neotoma cinerea*. Prevalent but seldom seen nocturnal pack rat or 'trade rat' (for habit of dropping one coveted item to pick up another) is ancient Canyon dweller. Busily builds 'middens,' complex nests of twigs, cactus, pine needles and cones.

Science of 'middenology' studies pack rat treasure piles stocked with seeds, bones, fruits, and pollen which, when fossilized over time, contain climate-revealing flora and fauna from prehistoric landscapes. Carbon dating sets some Canyon pack rat middens at more than 50,000 years old.

NATIONAL PARK SERVICE

Big-eared Bat -*Plecotus townsendii*. Long-eared, medium-sized bat, one of 20 Canyon species. Swift, adept flyers emerge from cracks, crevices, caves in early evening to forage on flying insects, mosquitoes.

ALLEN GILBERG

American Avocet -*Recurvirostra americana.* Transient flocks of up to 200 frequent Canyon on spring and fall migrations. Skims insects and plant matter from shallow water with sweeping motion of upward-curving bill.

PEREGRINE FUND

Peregrine Falcon -*Falco peregrinus.* Prefers open country; nests in cliffs. Preys on ducks and small birds with its sharp eyes, lethal talons, swift, vertical dive. Dramatic increase in numbers in recent years.

YOUNG CAGE

American Kestrel -*Falco sparverius.* Jay-sized falcon the former 'sparrow hawk,' is commonly seen in Canyon and along river. Year-round resident nests on cliffs, ledges. Hunts on the wing, hovering for small vertebrates, insects.

ALLEN GILBERG

Great Blue Heron -*Ardea herodias.* Largest North American heron (4 feet). Patient hunter makes lightning strikes at crustaceans and fish. Grasps prey with long, knifelike beak.

PETER LATOURRETTE

Bald Eagle -*Haliaeetus leucocephalus.* Canyon transient seen mostly in winter. Feeds on fish, waterfowl, carrion, spawning Nankoweap Creek trout. White head and tail denote adulthood.

ALLEN GILBERG

Common Raven -*Corvus corax.* Canyon character rides thermals, sometimes upside down. Scavenges campsites for leftovers, hillsides for carrion.

Commonly seen along the river

Migrating ducks such as mergansers are seen on the river throughout the year. The sandpiper is the most common shorebird seen in summer; the dipper or water ouzel is a permanent resident, seen especially in sidestreams.

Spotted Sandpiper -*Actitis macularia*

Common Merganser -*Mergus merganser*

American Dipper -*Cinclus mexicanus*

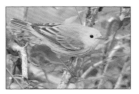

Yellow Warbler
Dendroica petechia

Blue-gray Gnatcatcher
Polioptila caerulea

Lazuli Bunting
Passerina amoena

Black Phoebe
Sayornis nigricans

Common Yellowthroat
Geothlypis trichas

Blue Grosbeak
Pheucticus melanocephalus

Say's Phoebe
Sayornis saya

Bell's Vireo
Vireo bellii

Commonly seen nesting riparian birds

Lush vegetation along the river, and on creeks, seeps and springs in the Canyon offers nesting sites in a desert environment for many colorful songbirds. Observant boaters and hikers may catch close-up views of these Canyon beauties.

PHOTOS ON THIS PAGE BY:
PETER LATOURRETTE
WWW.BIRDPHOTOGRAPHY.COM

NATURAL HISTORY

REPTILES AND AMPHIBIANS

Banded Gecko
Coleonyx variegatus.
Soft-skinned, short-limbed lizard. Active nocturnally. Feeds on insects, other small invertebrates. Sustained by fat stored in tail.

YOUNG CAGE

YOUNG CAGE

Red Spotted Toad -*Bufo punctatus.*
Small, nocturnal desert stream and pool dweller. Marked by red or orange warts, high-pitched trill heard from water's edge. Stays underground by day.

YOUNG CAGE

BILL BELKNAP

Woodhouse's Toad -*Bufo woodhousii.* Sizable, (to 4 inches) warty-skinned toad. Active by night; burrows by day. Bleeting, primordial call sounds along riverbanks toward evening.

Canyon Treefrog -*Hyla arenicolor.*
Small, rough-skinned frog with oversized, adhesive toe pads. Climbs rocks, trees to dine on bugs, beetles. Short, trilled song. Found perched on rocks and at water's edge on warm evenings.

KENTON GRUA

YOUNG CAGE

California King Snake -*Lampropeltis getulus.*
Regal-looking snake 2-4 feet long. Hunts in the cool of dawn, dusk and night. Feeds on rodents, lizards, snakes; immune to rattlesnake venom.

Red Coachwhip -*Masticophis flagellum.*
Diurnal, showy 'Red Racer' is alert, fast-moving. Preys on mice, lizards, small snakes. Common in side canyon brush.

YOUNG CAGE

YOUNG CAGE

Great Basin Gopher Snake -*Pituophis melanoleucus.*
Long (up to 6 feet) diurnal constrictor. Dwells in dry
sandy areas, side canyon brush. Feeds on rodents,
rabbits, birds. Stunning tan and dark brown pattern.
Agile climber and burrower. Avoids extreme heat.

Western Ground Snake -*Sonora semiannulata.* Small (to 15 inches) snake variable in coloration and pattern: from bands to stripes or solids. Primarily nocturnal. Feeds on spiders, scorpions, crickets, small insects. Prefers arid habitats: canyon rims, talus slopes, patches of desert shrub.

ALLEN GILBERG

CHARLY HEAVENRICH

Desert Spiny Lizard -*Sceloporus magister.* Common 'pushup' lizard seen in various Canyon habitats. Rough backward-pointing scales. Varicolored head or sides sometimes tinged with orange. Blue patches on throat and sides of belly especially prominent in males. Does 'pushups' exposing hidden body sites to target audiences: competitors, predators, mates.

Grand Canyon Rattlesnake -*Crotalus oreganus abyssus.* Several venomous rattlesnake species are found in Grand Canyon. The endemic GC 'Pink' is most commonly seen along the river. Dwells in riparian areas, on talus slopes, in side canyons; Seen in cool of early morning, evening. Up to 3 feet long. To avoid, watch placement of hands, feet.

Collared Lizard -*Crotaphytus collaris.* Colorful, active, flashy. When chased, sprints on hind legs, with forelegs and tail in air. Sometimes eats other lizards or small mice as well as insects.

CHARLY HEAVENRICH

CHARLY HEAVENRICH

Western Chuckwalla -*Sauromalus ater.*
Flat and fat. Suns on warm rocks close to
protective crevices. When threatened, darts
into crevice and gulps air to wedge itself
in. Largely herbivorous.

NATURAL HISTORY

FLOWERS - CACTI

KEVIN HARRIS

IRENE BRENNAN / KATE WATTERS inset

Buckhorn Cholla -*Cylindropuntia acanthocarpa.* Seen from Phantom Ranch downstream. Easy to distinguish cylindrical stems. Indians once steamed flower buds for food.

ALLEN GILBERG

California Barrel Cactus -*Ferocactus cylindraceus.* Large accordion-pleated stem expands as plant absorbs water. Stout spines live up to Latin-based name meaning fierce.

Many-Headed Barrel Cactus -*Echinocactus polycephalus.* Multiple stems and white cottony fibers on flowers and fruits. Found on south-facing slopes and ledges throughout the Canyon.

KATE WATTERS

BILL BELKNAP

Grizzly-Bear Prickly-Pear -*Opuntia polyacantha.* Magenta or yellow blossoms set off this inner Canyon cactus. Indians used fruit, flesh, spines, stems for food, healing, fishing, art.

Brown-Spined Prickly-Pear -*Opuntia phaeacantha.* Low growing cactus with spreading pads (modified stems). Flowers usually yellow but also pink. Fruit makes syrup, jelly, and candy.

Beavertail Cactus -*Opuntia basilaris*. Flat shape resembles beaver's tail. Lacks long spines. Numerous short, barbed bristles can surprise the unwary if touched.

Teddy-Bear Cholla Cactus -*Cylindropuntia bigelovii*. Dense, interlacing spines provide summer shade, buffer, from winter cold. Found on gravelly slopes in western Grand Canyon.

Corkseed Pincushion Cactus -*Mammillaria tetrancistra*. Nipple-like projections on stems, fishhook-shaped spines, identify this cactus. Smooth fruit; flowers often encircle top of stem.

Fishhook Cactus -*Mammillaria grahamii*. Pink flowers crown spiny stem of 'pincushion' cactus. Grows in sandy soils of side canyons, washes, flats and slopes throughout the Canyon.

Claret-Cup Cactus -*Echinocereus triglochidiatus*. Clusters of showy red springtime flowers of claret-cup cactus are seen on rocky slopes and ledges in Canyon and side canyons.

Engelmann Hedgehog Cactus -*Echinocereus engelmannii*. Abundant, low-growing cacti, typically seen in Inner Gorge; flowers in April, May. Bees and insects pollinate blossoms; mammals and birds feast on fruits and seeds.

FLOWERS - WHITE

KRISTIN HUISINGA / GEOFF GOURLEY inset

DAVID INOUYE

Sand Verbena -*Abronia elliptica*. Commonly found on sandy riverbanks; fragrant flowers open in early evening, close at sunup, conserving moisture during midday heat.

Prickly-Poppy -*Argemone munita*. Often mistaken for thistles without its flowers; sharp leaves and stems deter herbivores, delicate flowers attract pollinators.

LISA HAHN

JOSEPH BENNION

Sacred Datura -*Datura meteloides*. Large, showy white flowers; dangerous hallucinogenic properties. Also called Jimsonweed. Member of potato family. Night blooming.

KATE WATTERS

Tufted Evening Primrose -*Oenothera caespitosa*. Night blooming; white flowers turn pink; wilt in morning sun. Night-flying insects pollinate fragrant blossoms.

Pale Evening-Primrose -*Oenothera pallida*. Fragrant flowers and sucrose-rich nectar draw hawk moths to feed and depart dusted in pollen at sundown. Found on beaches and sand dunes.

Matted Tiquilia -*Tiquilia latior.* Low growing plant. Bristly leaves rise from woody taproot. Small, pink-white, funnel-shaped flowers. Widespread on beaches, dunes, slopes.

Mariposa Lily -*Calochortus flexuosus.* Flourishes on open desert patches in Canyon after spring rains. Pink-white flowers; grasslike leaves.

Desert Pincushion -*Chaenactis stevioides.* Wooly annual blooms from March to May. Grows on sandy beaches and desert slopes; mainly seen from Lees Ferry to Hance Rapid.

Spiny Aster -*Chloracantha spinosa.* Tall, broom-like herb forms dense thickets on beaches and bars the length of the Canyon. Daisylike flowers attract bees and butterflies.

Twining Milkweed -*Sarcostemma cynan-choides.* One of few vines found in inner Canyon. Twining stems; milky juice. Pale white to light purple flowers; fragrant.

Fleabane Daisy -*Erigeron sp.* Found from upper parts of inner Canyon to rim. Daisy-like appearance; member of sunflower family. Blooms April to October.

FLOWERS - CREAMY WHITE

KATE WATTERS

Banana Yucca - *Yucca baccata.* Waxy bell-shaped blossoms. Used by early Native Americans for food, shampoo, fibers. Found in upper reaches of Canyon.

JOHN DEWINE

Soaptree Yucca -*Yucca elata.* Rosettes of swordlike leaves top shaggy trunk. Indians mixed roots, stems, water for soap. Seen from Badger Rapid to Havasu.

BILL BELKNAP

Newberry's Yucca -*Hesperoyucca newberryi.* Seen at river level beginning at Stone Creek (Mile 131.5); bluish, bayonet-like leaves. Towering stalk sometimes visible from space.

ALTA HANSEN

Beargrass -*Nolina microcarpa.* Clumps of grasslike leaves; tall long-lasting flowering stalks. Seen on Canyon rocky slopes, open waterways. Indians used leaves for rope, mats.

Phragmites, Common Reed -*Phragmites australis.* Lining the riverbanks, this flowering, cornfield-like grass is often mentioned in Native American creation stories. Stems and leaves were used for mats, roofing, and arrow shafts.

Rock Nettle -*Eucnide urens.* Grows in rock crevices on Canyon walls, especially in lower reaches of the river corridor. Covered with bristly hairs that sting.

Century Plant -*Agave utahensis.* One of few plants found from rim to river. Blooms once between 20-40 years of age, then dies. Indians used for food, fiber, medicine beverages.

Long-Leaf Brickellbush -*Brickellia longifolia.* Varnished foliage; tiny, fragrant white blossoms in fall. Sunflower family member. Upright shrub grows on rocky talus slopes and cliffs. Seen along dry drainages and in side canyons.

Cryptantha -*Cryptantha* species. Easily identified by bristly hairs on stems and leaves and coiled arrangement of tiny four-petaled flowers. Found in sandy washes and on gravelly slopes.

FLOWERS - YELLOW

LISA HAHN

LISA HAHN

Prince's-Plume -*Stanleya pinnata*. Tall, eye-catching wands of yellow flowers; found on steep, rocky slopes; member of mustard family.

Golden Columbine -*Aquilegia chrysantha*. Perennial herb found in shady sidestream habitats—Vasey's Paradise, Elves Chasm.

MERIBETH RIFFEY

KATE WATTERS

Broom Snakeweed -*Gutierrezia sarothrae*. Tiny heads with both yellow disc and ray flowers. Once used medicinally and as treatment for snakebite. Poisonous to grazing animals.

Rabbitbrush -*Ericameria nauseosa*. Yellow flowers on small shrub seen most commonly in upper elevations of Canyon. Often confused with look alike, Broom Snakeweed.

KATE WATTERS

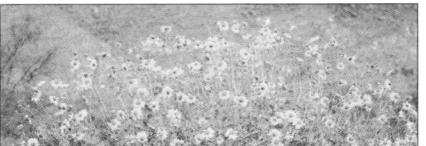

MERIBETH RIFFEY

Brittlebush -*Encelia farinosa*. Showy in spring-time on sun-exposed Canyon slopes. Easily broken stems ooze pungent, sticky substance.

Fetid-Marigold, Dogweed -*Thymophylla pentachaeta* var. *pentachaeta*. Small, compact herb, bright yellow daisy-like flowers. Often found growing near creosote and snakeweed.

Desert Senna - *Senna covesii.* Showy yellow flowers, long brown pods. Pea family member. Seen in gravelly washes, talus slopes, sandy beaches. Bees critical to pollination.

Grand Canyon Rock Daisy -*Perityle congesta.* Robust, multi-branched herb. Tiny yellow disk flowers. Thrives from river to rim, clinging to rock crevices.

Goldenbush, Jimmyweed -*Isocoma acradenia.* Common inner Canyon plant; blends with other desert plants until abundant late summer flowering. Indians used for fencing and kindling.

Desert Marigold -*Baileya multiradiata.* Grows in sandy soil or gravelly washes. Woolly leaves at base. Brilliant yellow flowers bloom through summer into fall.

Spiny Goldenweed -*Machaeranthera pinnatifida.* Bristly tips on small leaves, bracts enclosing flower head distinguish this one of many Canyon yellow composites. Found in gravelly soils, canyon bottoms, slopes.

Blackbrush -*Coleogyne ramosissima.* Compact shrub dominates transitional zone between warm and cold deserts on Tonto Plateau. Blooms March to May. Shelters insects, spiders, birds and mammals.

FLOWERS - RED/PURPLE

LISA HAHN

BILL BELKNAP

Globemallow -*Sphaeralcea grossulariifolia.* With ample moisture, blooms almost year-round in Inner Gorge. Hopi Indians used medicinally, chewed as gum.

KRISTIN HUISINGA

Cardinal Monkeyflower -*Mimulus cardinalis.* Grows in moist soil, shady seeps, sidestreams. Seen at favorite river stops—Vasey's Paradise, Elves Chasm, Havasu. Snapdragon-like flower.

Scarlet Lobelia, Cardinal Flower -*Lobelia cardinalis.* Grows near streams, seeps, and springs. Brilliant flowers in green riparian foliage draw hummingbirds as pollinators.

KATE WATTERS

KATE WATTERS

Common Paintbrush -*Castilleja applegatei.* Displays splash of color in spring and summer. Tolerates hot, dry, sandy soils, talus slopes at all elevations. Partially parasitic.

Purple Sage -*Salvia dorrii* ssp. *dorrii.* Bright flowers, aromatic essence of sage make this a springtime showstopper. Found on flats and in side canyons like Cardenas, Stone, Tapeats.

LISA HAHN

KATE WATTERS

Arrow-Weed -*Pluchea sericea.* Riparian shrub found the length of the river. Indians used silvery green leaves, long straight branches for arrow shafts, basketry, roof thatch.

Desert Four O'Clock -*Mirabilis multiflora.* Magenta to purple flower clusters open late in day. Found on dry slopes and desert flats length of river. Robust root used for medicinal uses.

GEOFF GOURLEY

KATE WATTERS

Filaree, Storksbill -*Erodium cicutarium.* Clusters of basal leaves, tiny pink flowers develop into beaklike fruit that toss seeds into air, which then drill into ground. Abundant in Canyon.

Arizona Centaury -*Centaurium arizonicum.* Delicate pink to magenta flowers with yellow stamens. Commonly seen in Canyon on riverbanks and in some sidestreams.

KATE WATTERS

KATE WATTERS

Purple Scorpionweed -*Phacelia crenulata.* Lower clusters curl, resembling scorpion's tail. Best left untouched—hairy leaves cause allergic reaction in some people.

Silverleaf Nightshade -*Solanum elaeagnifolium.* Noxious weed seen in disturbed areas. Silvery leaves, nodding purple flowers, protruding yellow anthers. Abundant on trails near Phantom Ranch.

NATURAL HISTORY

NATURAL HISTORY PICTORIAL GUIDE

TREES AND SHRUBS

NPS PHOTO - LORI MAKARICK / KATE WATTERS inset

Emory's Seep-Willow -*Baccharis emoryi*. Openly branched shrub 1 to 5 meters tall found along the riverbanks the length of the Canyon. Leaves blue-green in color with three to five large blunt teeth at the tip.

CELIA SOUTHWICK / LISA HAHN inset

Desert Broom -*Baccharis sarothroides*. Erect shrub 1 to 4 meters tall. Leaves linear, reduced to small bracts on upper stems. Widely used by Native Americans for food, fuel, weapons, building material.

KRISTIN HUISINGA

Coyote Willow -*Salix exigua*. Hardy riparian native shrub/tree found along side creeks and riverbanks. Sweet smelling flowers. Early Indians twisted young stems into split twig figurines.

KATE WATTERS

Baccharis, Seep-Willow -*Baccharis salicifolia*. Openly branched shrub 1 to 5 meters tall has finely toothed, shiny green sticky resinous leaves. *Emoryi* and *salicifolia* are showy in fall when white pappus of the fruits is prominent.

KATE WATTERS

Western Redbud -*Cercis orbiculata*. Delicate pink to magenta flowers in spring adorn this deciduous beauty found in shady, moist side canyons and on slopes along the river.

LISA HAHN

Netleaf Hackberry -*Celtis laevigata* var. *reticulata*. Huge tree with spreading crown atop stout, gnarled trunk. Grows in canyon bottoms and along pre-dam high water line.

Mesquite -*Prosopis glandulosa.* Grows on slopes and along washes, often with catclaw. Armed with long, straight, paired spines. Narrow bean-shaped pods rounded and straight.

Catclaw -*Acacia greggii.* Curving claw-like spines of "wait-a-minute bush" often catch clothing. Leaflets smaller than those of mesquite. Seed pods flat and twisted.

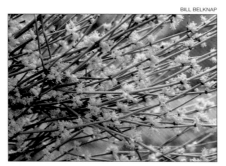

Mormon Tea -*Ephedra sp.* Also known as joint-fir because of its numerous jointed branches. Provides browse for animals; used medicinally by desert folk for many years.

Horsetail, Scouring Rush -*Equisetum x ferrissii.* River edge fern. Rough, hollow, jointed, strawlike stems. Fossil records date to dinosaur era. Stems used to scour dirty pots and pans.

Apache Plume -*Fallugia paradoxa.* Shrubs seen near old highwater line along river. Some Native Americans used stems for arrow shafts, brewed hair growth potion from leaves.

Creosote Bush -*Larrea tridentata.* Widely distributed desert shrub. May emit root toxins to protect its territory. Responsible for pungent aroma after desert downpour.

Bill Belknap

"No matter how much it has been improved since the days of Daguerre, the camera is never as important as the taste and imagination of the man who uses it."

George P. Hunt, Managing Editor,
Life Magazine, 1964

CHARLY HEAVENRICH

Pre-expedition advice

"Read the instructions and practice before you leave home."

Lynn Evans Peesel

Pre-expedition advice— *"I blew it! None of my pictures came out!"* The best way to avoid this problem, with a digital or film camera, is to test equipment at home *before* you go on a big trip or shoot any picture you really care about. Here are a few hints that will make picture taking more fun and ensure better success:

• Test your camera by taking photos outdoors and in different levels of light. Have your test photos printed or processed *before* going on your trip.

• Keep gear simple—beware of gadgets and features you don't understand. Read the instructions and practice before you leave home.

• Make the most of the technology you have: many digital cameras have sophisticated features allowing you to take still shots, panoramas, 360-degree images, or videos. Be familiar with what your camera can do.

• No matter what camera you use, bring extra memory cards or film and plenty of batteries!

ALLEN GILBERG

The magic of good picture taking

"'Be ready' is the photographer's motto."

Bill Belknap

The magic of good picture taking— A successful picture must do something to the person looking at it. It must cause a strong reaction—compassion, sadness, inspiration, joy, laughter. If the idea behind a picture is exciting enough, the quality doesn't have to be perfect. Zero in on the idea that inspired you to take the picture in the first place.

Lots of people excuse lousy pictures by saying they are "record shots." Pictures don't have to be dull, scientific, or just "for the record." Successful pictures usually combine a good idea with an exciting design. This can take practice. Have fun taking interesting photos that you are eager to share.

CHARLY HEAVENRICH

Semper Paratus

Semper Paratus—**"Be ready"** is the photographer's motto. Bring a camera you can keep fairly handy. Camera cases and lens caps can get in the way and can keep out good pictures. Being mentally ready is the most important. Think ahead to what'll probably happen and be ready for it!

MARK PEESEL

Give pictures, don't just take them

Give pictures, don't just take them—Have fun—it'll show in your pictures. Think about the poor victim who will be looking at them back home.

Keep shooting and use your best shot. The real thrill in photography is that no matter how experienced you get, you still have surprises and you always keep learning. Digital cameras allow you to take multiple pictures of the same thing and then share only the best with friends and family at home. Digital cameras also provide instant feedback so you can retake shots until you get the best image possible.

"Great photo –what camera did you use?"

"Great photo–what camera did you use?" This commonly asked question is much like asking the writer of a good story what kind of computer he used. It's not uncommon for folks to see a picture they like, find out the brand of camera it was shot with, and then rush out and buy that camera–hoping it'll do the same for them. It seldom does. Make the most of the camera you have.

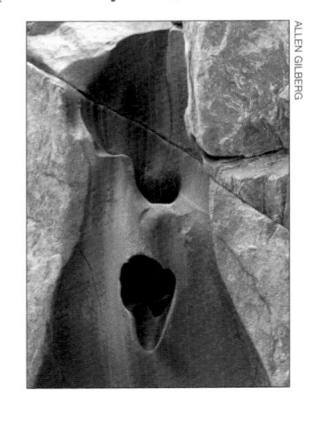

ALLEN GILBERG

Tools, tricks and techniques

Tools, tricks and techniques for great river photos—

Lighting: Be ready to capture the ever-changing light and moods of the Canyon. Use early or

ALLEN GILBERG

"Tilt the camera slightly upriver to give the feeling that the river is really flowing downhill...."

late afternoon sun to bring out shapes and textures. Backlighting your photos adds a dramatic touch.

Canyon shots: Things look taller or deeper if you lop off the top so your viewers have to guess how high it is — this is true for canyon walls, waterfalls and mountains.

Rapid shots: You can make rapids look as exciting as they really are by following a few simple guidelines:

1. Tilt the camera slightly upriver to give the feeling that the river is really flowing downhill — don't overdo it so it looks fake.

2. Shoot from water level. Even get down in the water if possible.

3. Try to get some fast and furious water action in the foreground close to the camera and have a boat partly hidden behind a wave.

Note: The rapid-fire function on many cameras today is a great feature for recording all the thrills and spills.

CHARLY HEAVENRICH

ALLEN GILBERG

ALLEN GILBERG

The professional approach

"The bad pictures you don't show can't be used against you."

Bill Belknap

"A pro uses all the testing, rehearsing, backups, and pre-planning possible . . . a pro never stops experimenting."

Bill Belknap

The professional approach—a closeup. A pro is always thinking how to get his camera where nobody has ever had a camera before. He is someone who never shows anybody his mistakes. When a pro blows a picture he throws it away or deletes it. The bad pictures you don't show can't be used against you.

A pro uses all the testing, rehearsing, backups, and pre-planning possible. The only way anybody can be sure is to experiment. Use backups wherever you can. Make several shots–pros often carry more than one camera, or at the very least, multiple memory sticks. And a pro *never* stops experimenting.

If you've brought a camera that has a really good zoom lens, and many of today's digital cameras do, make the most of it, whether it's going for a closeup of a rare canyon blossom, or catching an on-the-run shot of a California condor.

The real thrill in photography is that no matter how experienced you get, you still never *really* know how a picture's going to turn out! Digital view screens give you a pretty good sense of composition, but there are always surprises, especially when it comes to lighting and color. There's always plenty to learn!

JUSTIN HOWE

ALLEN GILBERG

Chaos in the computer

Chaos in the computer, or what do you do with your pictures at home? Have you come home from a trip, downloaded photos, and then didn't know what to do next? Just because you've taken a picture doesn't mean you have to save it for the rest of your life. Whether digital or film, you can throw away the bad ones. Whether you print your own photos or have them printed, choose a selection of the very best to show to your friends and family. Make it interesting to *them*, not *you*.

Use lots of variety — long, medium, close-up, and macro shots will spice up your photos. Move in tight on faces. Look for exciting color combinations and interesting patterns.

There are many online resources that can make prints and albums for you. It's fun to have a first-rate selection of photos to share, but remember to always quit while you're ahead. Leave your audience pleading — begging for more!

"Use lots of variety—long, medium, close-up, and macro."
Bill Belknap

"Always quit while you're ahead. Leave your audience pleading— begging for more."
Bill Belknap

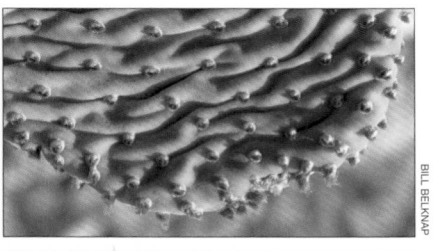

BILL BELKNAP

LISA HAHN

KATE WATTERS

Bill Belknap

HISTORY NOTE
Beginning with Major Powell as the 1st person to go down the Grand Canyon in 1869, Bill Belknap was the 114th to traverse the canyon in 1950.

THE RIM CONNECTION
Bill's mother was part owner of **Grand Canyon Boulder Dam Tours** in Boulder City, offering early boating and plane tours of the Canyon.

Bill's father-in-law, Frank Spencer was Fred Harvey's manager of the **Hopi House** from 1919 to 1955.

A native of New York State, Bill Belknap was born with an incurable interest in everything Indian. He moved west at an early age and spent every possible moment at Grand Canyon and with the Hopi Indians. It was here that he met Frances Spencer, his future bride and life-long partner.

During World War II he trained at *Life* magazine and served as White House photographer for the U.S. Navy. Later, he photographed and wrote for *National Geographic* and other publications. He and Fran co-authored *Gunnar Widforss, Painter of the Grand Canyon*. It was followed by *Fred Kabotie: Hopi Indian Artist, an autobiography with Bill Belknap*.

Through meeting and photographing some of the legendary Grand Canyon river people, such as Emery Kolb, Buzz Holmstrom, Norm Nevills, and Dock Marston, Bill became deeply involved in river running. Beginning in the late 1940s, he participated in, photographed, and wrote extensively about his Canyon adventures.

In 1969, Bill's son Buzz enlisted his father's help to create the first *Grand Canyon River Guide*. That teamwork led to the establishment of a family publishing company, Westwater Books, which continues to produce this Guide and others for river runners today.

Together with Fran and daughter Loie Belknap Evans, Bill also ran Fastwater Expeditions, a river company that offered full-participation Sportyak trips on the Green, San Juan, and Dolores Rivers.

Bill Belknap loved people and sharing with them the things he cherished most—the Colorado and its canyons, deserts, Indians, and photography.

HAND-TINTED PHOTOGRAPH, BELKNAP COLLECTION

Thomas Moran and Frances Spencer (Belknap)
at Hopi House, South Rim, about 1920. Moran provided many of the illustrations for John Wesley Powell's official 1875 report; his paintings popularized the Canyon and helped inspire the creation of Grand Canyon National Park.

THE CREW

Buzz Belknap

Loie Evans

Buzz Belknap, mastermind behind the Westwater Books River Guide series, was introduced to river running by his father, Bill Belknap. Buzz's Canyon adventures include a 1958 outboard expedition riding flows in excess of 100,000 c.f.s. and a 1963 sportyak trip on 900 c.f.s. He crewed for the 1959 Disney film, *Ten Who Dared*, a reenactment of Powell's journey, and, at sixteen, piloted one of four jet boats on the 1960 Grand Canyon uprun.

Loie Belknap Evans, also co-author of the other River Guides in the series, is president of Westwater Books, headquartered in Evergreen, Colorado. As a licensed river guide, she played a key role in Fastwater Expeditions, a family-owned river business that featured full participation trips in individually rowed Sportyaks. Loie loves sharing her interests in the canyons and rivers with friends and family.

Wayne Ranney is a geologist, author and international lecturer whose books and articles on the geology of the Grand Canyon have brought it to life in new ways for everyone from river passengers to university professors. In addition to teaching geology at Coconino Community College in Flagstaff, Arizona, Wayne leads backcountry adventures and expeditions around the world. For details see: www.WayneRanney.com

Lynn Evans Peesel, whose information on how to successfully use your digital camera in the Canyon appears on page 120, is the newest member of the editorial team, adding her knowledgeable eye drawn from years of river boating experience. Her husband Mark, and daughters Zoe and Spencer share her love of the rivers.

Douglas W. Schwartz, widely recognized as the pioneering archeologist and anthropologist of the Grand Canyon and Southwest, conducted research and major Canyon excavations on the Unkar Delta, Bright Angel Delta, and Walhalla Plateau. From 1967-2001 Doug directed the School for Advanced Research (SAR) in Santa Fe, an innovative organization supporting advanced research, writing, and publishing in the field of anthropology. http://sarweb.org. Doug passed away in 2016.

Meribeth M. Riffey was a biology professor and ornithologist who introduced river travelers to the natural history of the Grand Canyon through workshops she conducted for many years. She and her husband, John Riffey, longtime ranger for Grand Canyon National Park, lived in the Toroweap Valley.

Jodi Parry Belknap co-editor of this Guide, has been a mainstay on the *Grand Canyon River Guide* team since its inception in 1969. A writer and designer, she owned Belknap Publishing and Design.

OTHER MAJOR CONTRIBUTORS

George Billingsley, **Brad Dimock**, and **Richard Quartaroli**—all have decades of Grand Canyon and Colorado River experience—boating, guiding, hiking, photographing, geologizing, writing, and consulting—they have become part of the Canyon's history! **George** is perhaps best known for almost single-handedly mapping the geology of the entire lower Grand Canyon and discovering the Surprise Canyon Formation. **Brad** might be best known for his research and understanding of early river pioneers, publishing their biographies, and re-creating the boats they used. **Richard** is known and revered for his vast historical knowledge of the Canyon and finding ways to share it with others. All three have been honored with the prestigious Grand Canyon Historical Society Pioneer Award, and each has been featured in issues of the Grand Canyon River Guides *Boatman's Quarterly Review*. Their invaluable help has enhanced this River Guide. For more information on this trio see: www.grandcanyonhistory.org/awards.html; and http://www.gcrg.org/bqr.php

RIVER LOG

BILL BELKNAP